A Clean Grassy Space

one strange journey to becoming a
veterinarian

by Lee R. Harris, DVM

Dedicated to fellow creatures of all species that accompanied my journey through veterinary school, and above all to my wife, Terri, who has been my constant support.

CONTENTS

1

Preface

Looking far back in memory is like peering through the wrong end of a telescope. On the page everything seems smaller and farther away than it felt fifty years ago. But recalling those experiences reverses the telescope to reveal details close up that were not appreciated at the time. Such is the nature of remembrance.

Contemplating through the looking glass I see my young self more clearly than I could have at the time. In the era of my youth, social awkwardness, anxiety, and crippling shyness were merely considered features of an individual's personality, if considered at all. It rarely occurred to parents or teachers that peculiarities were something to be labelled or changed, and Dr. Asperger would not describe his high-functioning version of social impairment until I had almost passed childhood.

Veterinary medicine reached out to me, although I never anticipated the combination of TV doctor heroics, cattle roundup wrangling, scientific geekiness, old-fashioned practicality, and freewheeling charity that it involved. I found myself on a path that wound thru strange and unfamiliar territory for which I was unprepared. Perhaps that is true for each of us; I can only speak for myself.

As memoirs go, this story is more mundane than dramatic. No tales of neglect, no substance abuse, no dangers on the mean streets, no dysfunctional family (at least by the standards of most memoirs), but to me it felt like an alien journey of discovery. Here is what I remember.

2

Bones

A drop of red blood fell onto the stainless steel surface in front of me, and I knew immediately that it hadn't come from the dog on the table. The body was that of a canine cadaver, preserved for dissection, but the thumb was my own. I could feel the sting of formaldehyde in the cut but paused for only a moment; I had only just begun, and there was a lot of work ahead.

On this first day of veterinary school, disassembling the tissues of an animal's body with surgical instruments was new and I had no idea how sharp a scalpel blade actually was. Surprisingly little pressure was needed to slice thru the cadaver's skin and into my thumb, opening the first of many self-inflicted wounds. Someday these hands would be those of a surgeon, but now they felt curiously unfamiliar as they separated muscle from bone, traced nerves along their courses, searched for something recognizable in the inner recesses of the body.

My shiny new dissecting instruments gave the sense of power that comes from having the right tools. Each student was required to buy a simple set of surgical instruments to use for dissection: a scalpel handle with a supply of razor-sharp blades, a pair of Mayo dissecting scissors with slightly rounded tips for bluntly separating tissues, and a pair of thumb forceps—no, please don't call them "tweezers", although they look like splinter-removing gadgets with little teeth at the end. Veterinary students affected the vernacular of experienced surgeons and called them "pick-ups", since they were used to pick up pieces of tissue. With professional surgical instruments, we could almost imagine that we were performing some complex surgical procedure; now, if only we could find the gall bladder on our dog specimen!

This cadaver had once been a stray, but it had been euthanized at a shelter in Idaho after no owner could be found—a common fate of homeless animals. In life the body had belonged to a dark tan dog of mixed ancestry with the medium-length muzzle of a herding breed. To my surprise I was not distressed by dissecting an animal whose life must have had its own history of love or tragedy. It simply seemed unreal, far removed from the familiar breathing and beating of life. Perhaps this was due to the lack of blood, which had been drained from the vessels and replaced with colored latex, red rubbery material in the arteries and blue in the veins. Perhaps the formaldehyde-preserved firmness of the tissues added to the strangeness, robbing the dog of the tenderness of living tissue.

Memory and smell are intricately linked, and the smell of formaldehyde, pungent and distinctive, was the hallmark of gross anatomy lab and the freshman veterinary students who spent their days hunched like curious vultures over their specimens. It was said among the English majors, architecture students, and future elementary school teachers at Washington State University that you never had to ask a freshman veterinary student what his major was; you could smell the formaldehyde from ten yards away. In 1970 nobody was concerned about the ill effects of formaldehyde exposure; it was only decades later that the government classified the preservative as a substance so hazardous that a building must be evacuated if a formaldehyde spill occurs.

I never noticed any ill effects from breathing the toxic fumes, although it is likely that my already poor olfactory senses were further diminished by formaldehyde exposure. This loss of smell would prove beneficial as my education would involve frequent intimate experience with the odors of excrement, pus, and diseased flesh. Anatomy students are now somewhat protected from the formaldehyde fumes by ventilation hoods, but we worked on open tables, bare-handed, sixty eager heads bent closely over our specimens for four hours a day, five days a week, for nine months. I shared my dissection table with three other students and we named our cadaver Fred.

On the first day of vet school, all of the freshmen vet students were given an orientation tour of the school facilities and the teaching hospital. (I will use the familiar "vet" in place of "veterinarian" at times, although we were warned that it was somehow disrespectful, and that using the twelve-letter word for animal doctor would confer more respect on the future Doctor of Veterinary Medicine. Pardon the use of the more familiar version throughout this memoir).

Our tour started in the Anatomy Museum, a bizarre suite of rooms which featured a preserved and lacquered cow stomach, mounted specimens of the lower legs of horses with each nerve and vessel neatly tagged and labelled, and a dog skull with each of the twelve cranial nerves dissected and preserved in a dehydrated tableau that in no way resembled any living tissue that we would ever see. There were also preserved specimens of veterinary freaks: two-headed lambs, deformed horse legs, and dog hearts with the major blood vessels attached in all the wrong places. Apparently when anything weird and creepy showed up in post-mortem, the pathologists thought that students deserved to see it. The walls were lined with shelves filled with jars of body parts in alcohol. Our guide helpfully offered that we were welcome to use the Anatomy Museum as a cozy place to do our studying. To me it seemed more creepy than cozy.

As our tour progressed through the small animal hospital, we saw dogs being prepared for surgery and sneezing cats with an isolation ward all to their miserable selves. As we proceeded through the postmortem room, we viewed the remains of those patients that did not leave through the hospital's front doors. In the large animal section of the hospital we were shown long corridors of scrubbed concrete stalls where equine patients relaxed amid the smells of hay, manure, and disinfectant. The horse surgery area was literally a spacious padded room with thick rubber pads on the floor and walls. Our tour guide told us that the greatest risk in equine surgery was that the horse would hurt itself by flailing around as it recovered from anesthesia. This was our first intimation of how easily even the most successful surgery could turn into a disaster.

For now, however, these were but apprehensive ghosts of the future.

The freshman orientation tour concluded with a brief speech by Dr. Henderson, who had been the dean of the veterinary school for decades. The usual encouraging words were spoken, but a lack of inspirational platitudes gave us to know that nothing would come easily or predictably. His final words foretold a hard truth: "Half of everything we teach you in the next four years will be untrue; the trouble is, we don't know which half."

Perhaps the only place where Dean Henderson's warning of obsolescent knowledge was not true was in Gross Anatomy. The physical structures of the body have been described in minute detail for centuries and they remain predictably entombed in the sacred texts of anatomy with their line-drawings and Latin names. True, there would be the occasional variation, and a student would call out to the lab instructor, "My dog doesn't have the anterior branch of the circumflex illiac artery", but most anomalies were due to insufficient diligence on the part of the student dissector.

The anatomy lab was a stark but well-lit second-floor room, tiled on both floor and walls, with a high ceiling and fifteen stainless steel tables arranged in two rows. There was no decor and no sounds other than the mumbling of the students who were seated, four to a table, around their dissection specimens. To any stranger who wandered into the lab it looked like a factory sweatshop, except that the smell was worse and objects were being taken apart rather than put together.

The definitive and unchanging nature of Gross Anatomy Lab suited me. I could bury myself in the anatomy texts and compare them to the once-living specimen in front of me without having to interact with the instructor or other students. I preferred to figure things out for myself and the answers were all cut and dried.

It had always seemed obvious to me that humans and other animals are constructed similarly and that any differences between our species were minor. As I separated my dog's quadriceps muscle from the vastus lateralis muscle, it never occurred to me that our own anatomy differed from the canine cadaver on the table in any meaningful way. In fact, the species differences were so infrequent that they were mentioned as points of interest: for instance, dogs lacked the clavicle, or collarbone of the human. The cat, however, had a vestige of the clavicle which could be seen on x-rays, but is so well hidden in the chest muscles that it is difficult to find it on dissection. Under the microscope the slight differences between our own bodies and those of the animals around us disappeared altogether. A liver cell looked like a liver cell, and to my eyes it was impossible to tell whether a hepatocyte came from a human, dog, or cow liver. Despite the close similarities, I often hear pet owners express surprise that their cat has a pancreas like a person's, or that the parts of their dog's brain have the same nerve connections as their own brain.

The study of anatomy was largely a matter of brute memorization, guided by the Grays's Anatomy bible of our profession, Miller's Anatomy of The Dog. Every body part was subdivided into detailed pieces: It was not enough to know that the upper bone of the forelimb was the humerus; every little bump on the bone deserved its own name. The greater tubercle was not to be confused with the lesser tubercle or the intertubercular groove. To know each muscle I needed to name its origin (where it came from) and its insertion (the end where it attaches to do its work); knowing where they started and ended told the story of what the muscles were meant to do. We all have our origins and insertions.

The first four-hour session in anatomy lab introduced 150 new names of structures to be memorized, with another hundred each succeeding day. The dissection of our dog's head alone took two months, every square inch traversed by a dozen tiny nerves, muscles, and arteries, each with their own Latin name.

I gained some minor advantage from having taken Latin as my foreign language option in high school. The "dead language" that was once the mark of the educated man was still good for one thing; the earliest anatomists would simply name structures by what they were: For instance, the little tube (ductus) that connects the main arteries (arteriosus) was simply called the ductus arteriosus. Anatomical names rolled off the tongue more easily for having struggled through two years of Latin vocabulary.

After completing five months with our dog cadaver we moved on to feline dissection, which took two days. Throughout veterinary school, cats seemed to receive scant attention; their popularity as household pets had not yet overtaken dogs as the country's favorite pet.

Halfway thru the year it was announced that our dissecting group would work with some actual live animals. After five months with only Fred for company, the prospect of touching flesh-and-blood creatures was exciting. But first we needed to get acquainted with large animal anatomy. Our cadavers were no longer spread on stainless steel tables. Instead, preserved bodies of horses and cattle were suspended from a ceiling track by heavy chains. When students were not at work dissecting the bodies the cadavers were rolled along the track into a large walk-in refrigerator to chill for the evening. By day a group of eight students would stand around each body, examining every part, inside and outside. Many structures were already familiar from the dog: muscles, bones, nerves, and blood vessels generally followed the mammalian blueprint. But inside, things were different. The entire interior of a cow appeared to be packed with a jumbled series of stomachs that had no canine or human analogue, while the horse has a sac-like cecum where the human appendix lies, but three feet long and packed with the end-products of digestion, an equine septic tank for the digestive tract. We were given to know that these unique abdominal structures were the source of all sorts of serious livestock ailments that we would come to know and love.

Studying the cold cadavers couldn't give us a feel for the internal structures of large animals, so live animals were introduced to our education.

The vet school maintained a small number of large animals for hands-on learning. The palpator cows were tired old Holsteins, dairy cattle that had reached the end of their milking careers. A few elderly horses that apparently nobody wanted also earned their keep by providing hands-on education.

The exciting prospect of touching real living animals faded quickly.

While resting my hand against the flank of a large black-and-white cow made me feel like part of the brotherhood of animal doctors, my bovine knowledge was limited to a collection of Latin words. The reason that the palpator cows were standing in stanchions in a concrete room behind the anatomy lab was so that we could learn the art of rectal palpation. By inserting one's arm up to the shoulder thru the anus and into the large intestine, various parts of the digestive tract and uterus could be felt. This would prove useful to determine if one of the stomachs was twisted out of place or if the uterus held a live calf. In principle it sounded simple, if not appealing.

First, a thin shoulder-length glove was pulled on over the long-sleeved overalls that we wore to Anatomy Lab every day. In those days veterinary students were required to wear a shirt and tie to all classes and labs, so I zipped up the overalls to cover my tie and pulled the rubber "OB sleeve" all the way up to my armpit. (We could always tell who the real cowboys were; they had overalls with the sleeves cut off and they sneered at the idea of using a glove, preferring the feel of their bare arm in the manure factory.) The next step was to move right up behind the cow and lift the tail. Although most of us were inexperienced, the palpator cows were not, and they did not quietly accept the insertion of the student's hand and arm into their rectum. We had been informed that, although horses kick straight behind them, cows can only kick off the to the side and we were in the safest position immediately behind the tail. These cows had apparently not read the manual, or they had been taking lessons from the horses; they seemed equally adept at landing a well-aimed kick from any angle. "The closer you stand, the less it hurts", we were told. As unprepared as we were to learn this bizarre new skill, the instructors simply told us where to find the cows and left us on our own. Some things just have to be learned by experience, so I patted the rump of the nearest cow and apologized in advance.

A long concrete gutter ran across the floor to make it easier to hose down the manure that fell where the cow was restrained, so I had to avoid a pile of cow dung as I perched with one foot on the edge of the trough, inching my other foot as close as I dared between the cow's rear hooves. Lifting the tail, I advanced my right hand into the anus, only to be slapped in the face with the manure-soiled tip of the tail. Pressing on, my arm slid into the rectum. I had expected that the internal organs would be closer, more distinct. Instead, it felt as if I was lost in a sack of warm, pungent oatmeal, and even the location of the intestinal wall was difficult to discern. At that moment, for the first time in my veterinary education, the thought flashed across my cerebral cortex: What am I doing here, and how did I get to this place? Was this what I had always wanted, or was I just being carried along by the momentum of old decisions? I didn't have long to ponder these questions, as the cow suddenly lashed out with its left hind leg. I dodged the hoof, but as I quickly pulled my arm from the rectum I lost my footing on the manure trough and went down on my back in the muck. The cow calmly resumed chewing a mouthful of hay.

Most of the anatomy learned this year would be lost to memory by the time I needed to use it, and a refresher course in my third year would serve as a reminder before I started to learn surgical skills. For now there was more to learn, and little time to question the direction that my course was taking.

3

A Boy's Life

In the dark-paneled waiting room a skinny eight-year-old boy picked up the Boy's Life magazine from February 1958. The dentist was busy working on his older brother, so there was plenty of time to leaf thru the magazine. One of the feature articles described an interesting career that a boy might consider: You could become an animal doctor. All you had to do was be good at school, interested in science, and like animals. Although his experience with animals was limited to a Cocker Spaniel that his family had owned for a few years and a snowy owl and a flying squirrel that had shared the house when he was a toddler, the boy was interested. By the time he had finished the article he decided that he wanted to be a veterinarian.

It is hard to know where life choices start. It may be that a particular aptitude pushes someone down their life path, or it may be that parental pressure guides the young person in a direction that a mother or father imagines will lead to success. Or direction may not develop until early adulthood forces a reluctant choice. For me it may have been that I was a sick child.

Doctors had diagnosed me with a congenitally malpositioned colon, as well as a mysterious heart murmur. At the age when earliest memories are preserved, all I remember are frequent bouts of intestinal pain. When frequent enemas and regular injections of Demerol couldn't control the cramping, my family moved from upstate New York to Denver, where surgeons were developing techniques to correct similar intestinal problems. The first surgery to untwist my colon came at four years of age; later that year complications ensued, with adhesions and gangrene of the intestine. Doctors told my parents that I had to have another surgery to remove large sections of the intestine that had lost circulation, but that I might not live. I survived, however, and the memories I have of each long post-surgical hospital stay are not unpleasant (except that I was unwilling to ask the nurses where the bathroom was until I was desperate). Recuperation kept me in a large ward at Children's Hospital shared by twenty other children. I never spoke to any of them, but as I recovered we would race our wheelchairs around the ward and laugh when we nearly upset the nurses' trays of medicine.

Although I found the dietary restrictions after surgery to be embarrassing (even after I started kindergarten, I could only eat Gerber's baby food, which prompted teasing from other kids), I found the explanations of my health problems fascinating. Even at an early age I understood what the intestine did, how much they had surgically removed and why, and the concept of probiotics (far ahead of my time, I took Lactinex tablets filled with helpful intestinal bacteria that were supposed to improve my digestion). My intestine never did function completely normally, and frequent embarrassing flatulence continued all my life.

Looking back I suppose that my medical history fueled an interest in how the body works and how it can be changed by medicine and surgery. Just as a new duckling imprints and follows the first object that it sees after hatching, I had imprinted on medicine and followed that interest to adulthood.

Why not become a human doctor? That question was asked frequently by well-meaning teachers and counselors. The answer was simple: I didn't like people. Or at least I lacked the social skills to make friends or ask questions of strangers. Among veterinary students it isn't unusual to hear the proclamation that "I like animals better than people", but my social anxiety went well beyond that statement. I thought that working with animals would suit me; it wasn't until much later that I realized how the veterinary profession involves close human relationships with people who love their animals.

I was fortunate to grow up with tolerant parents who were willing to allow their children the freedom to foster their own interests, and in a family of five children there wasn't enough time to smother any of us with excess attention. We mostly went our own way. Dad was an aerospace engineer and Mom was a homemaker (before that profession was reduced to "stay-at-home-mom"—she even had a college degree in Home Economics). My older brother was a lawyer who became a writer, one sister became an investigative writer while the other performs and teaches belly-dancing around the world. My younger brother used his artistic hands to create dental prostheses. Diverse interests kept us from being close, but there were very few family conflicts to color our childhoods.

In the middle of third grade a decisive change took our family from the suburbs of Denver to the small mountain town of Evergreen, where there were plenty of ponderosa pines, dirt roads, and undeveloped spaces. Few rules were enforced and we were allowed to roam freely in the woods and the adjacent cattle ranch.

And there was plenty of room for animals. We built a roomy corral and stocked it with a variety of riding horses: Tomahawk, a retired cowpony, Spook, a docile flea-bitten grey, Phantom, a spirited Arab-Quarter Horse cross, and Pepe, her Appaloosa-cross colt. Summers were spent riding trails in the hills, while winters were spent hauling hay and pouring hot water to keep the drinking trough open in sub-zero weather. We had a pair of Collies and raised several litters of puppies, which brought me into contact with Dr. Tony Anderson, who vaccinated our dogs in the kitchen of his farmhouse when he wasn't out on ranch calls. I used "I'm going to be a veterinarian" as an excuse to keep and breed dozens of hamsters, as well as keeping several three-striped ground squirrels that I live-trapped in our woods. I usually kept the wild rodents for only a few days, as they refused to be tamed and didn't enjoy confinement. This was probably a good thing, as I later learned that ground squirrels and chipmunks commonly carry the bacillus that causes the plague. All I knew was that they bit.

A move to Colorado Springs in the eighth grade forced us to sell our horses, but I kept my colony of hamsters. I added a number of gerbils, the Mongolian jumping mice that became popular pets in the early 60's. I had discovered the novel rodents in a pet store in Milwaukee during an unchaperoned visit to my grandmother and I smuggled them home aboard the airplane. I never told my parents about the addition to my rodent farm; they were just as happy not knowing. I had a mynah bird and later added a magpie that I had adopted as a chick from a nest in the scrub oak foothills west of town.

When our family moved again, this time to Seattle, I was allowed to bring my menagerie along. The trip resulted in several escape episodes along the way, including a half day spent trying to recapture my magpie in a field in the middle of Wyoming. I maintained my animal collection until I left for college. My mom refused to be a den mother to my collection of small mammals, but she did agree to care for my birds during my first year of college.

I don't recall having a great emotional attachment to the animals I kept; I was very interested in them, their lives and behavior, but I was not an "animal lover" in a sentimental way. Rather, I considered them as friends or acquaintances that were roughly co-equal to myself and who didn't require the conversation and interaction that humans demanded. Even in elementary school I had developed the firm opinion that animals were intelligent in their own way, conscious beings who had their own realities, desires, and emotions. At that time this position was considered naive anthropomorphism, the cardinal sin of biology. Intelligence is usually defined in our own image, by comparing how other organisms behave to our own way of living and then using the differences to claim our superiority. Linguists are particularly determined to claim language as a uniquely human trait. When it was discovered that animal sounds communicate emotions to other animals they insisted "but sounds are not words". When was shown that animal sounds have specific meanings, they countered that animal communication lacked grammar. And when animal vocalizations and body language turned out to have broadly grammatical functions, it seems that linguists would not be satisfied unless a non-human translation of Plato's Dialogues was discovered. Why the insistence on human superiority?

One reason may be that we are unable to share the experiences of non-human organisms and how they sense and understand their own worlds. How can we understand the mind of a bat or a porpoise that inhabits an environment filled with information written in echoes, or the thoughts of a dog to whom the past and present are simultaneously present in the smells that surround it?

It may also be that we humans have an innate need to feel superior. This seems to be true in our view of other human cultures, and even a glance at the last few centuries would echo the theme of "we are better than they are" when considering people who live and speak differently. Exceptionalism creates a delusion of power and the right to use that power for our own benefit. These youthful ideas were not sophisticated philosophical positions, but truths evident even to a perceptive high school student with an outsider's perspective.

As I viewed the relationship of humans and other animals, I had a different point of view. Based on my own easy academic success and high IQ scores, I felt I was in a position to judge the value of Intelligence (whatever that was), and I didn't see any "great divide" of human exceptionalism. To me, it seemed that the definition of success was simply how well an organism was suited its environment and lifestyle. Feeling alienated by struggling to understand people, I felt kinship with other misunderstood organisms.

Neuroscience has since gradually worn away some of these prejudices. and a wide variety of animals are now acknowledged to have their own sophisticated forms of consciousness, intelligence, and communication.

By the time I was in high school I was still firmly on the path toward veterinary medicine. I don't know if this persistence was because of my interest in animals or because I was not equipped to deal with changing my mind or considering other choices. I was fortunate that school came easily to me, thru no great effort on my part. I was particularly adept in science and math, and my overworked teachers were more than happy to promote me into advanced classes and let me skip classes to study on my own. Along with perfect grades I accumulated the sorts of minor academic awards that are intended to foster young talent.

Due to my academic success I was offered a summer research program for high school students at the University of Washington and spent the summer at the Pack Research Forest on the flanks of Mount Rainier. Since I had some experience with rodents, I chose to research the seed preferences of the mice that inhabited the forestry research area. When new Douglas fir seeds were planted at the forest nursery the seeds would always be quickly consumed by the meadow mice, voles, and pacific jumping mice in the forests and clearings. The foresters had tried putting out poisoned grain to reduce the number of rodents, but the mice ignored the grain and cleaned out every fir seed that was planted. My goal was to figure out what seeds the animals preferred, and why.

I was allowed to take over a corner of a field shack where a graduate student was doing tree respiration studies, a half-mile from the Pack Forest bunk house. I live-trapped the little creatures that frequented the meadow and brought them into my makeshift lab, where I kept each subject for an hour and offered a smorgasbord of different seeds and grains. After an hour I would record which seeds had been eaten, mark each mouse, and release it back into the woods. Every hour the process would be repeated, around the clock for four days every week. I learned two things: First, that mice really liked Douglas fir seeds; was it was their high fat content or the fact that they were a rare seasonal treat? (As with any good scientific paper, the report I presented at the end-of-summer gathering of students and professors concluded with "more research is indicated to answer these questions"). Secondly, I learned that academic science moves very slowly; the graduate student whose space I was sharing had been working on his project for three years and data was just starting to come in; in another year or two he would start trying to draw some conclusions. I knew that I needed more timely gratification than the life of a researcher offered, and it seemed that veterinary medicine offered the chance of seeing results as my patients recovered in days, not years.

The momentum of my career choice made me impatient. With no social or emotional ties to high school, I was ready to move on.

4

The Terrain

"Le terrain est tout." Louis Pasteur, father of the germ theory of disease, had a long-running argument with his rival, Antoine Bechamp, over the nature of infectious disease. Pasteur blamed bacteria for causing many of the diseases that plagued humanity, while Bechamp emphasized what we now call "host factors": Stress, nutritional deficiency, and weakness of the immune system allow otherwise innocent microorganisms to run amok. On his deathbed, Pasteur relented to Bechamp's point of view; his final words were reported to be "The microbe is nothing, the terrain is everything."

The terrain, the landscape in which we live our lives, influences whether we wither or thrive. For some, going away to college is simply an extension of high school, with more beer and less rules. For me it was a quest into a metaphorical wilderness filled with strange beasts and stranger people.

I never had the feeling that I led a sheltered life. Although I had never tasted alcohol, kissed a girl, or been to a party or a prom, it was not due to parental restrictions. Extreme shyness can easily be mistaken for good behavior and I simply avoided activities that involved interaction with strangers. I had backpacked alone in bear country on the Pacific coast, climbed on the glaciers of Mount Rainier, and even explored house jams in Seattle's African-American Central District to hear blues singers like Howlin' Wolf and Mississippi Fred McDowell, but these were activities that I could do by myself. My parents, although adventurous in their own ways, were from thoroughly plain midwestern stock; they didn't smoke, drink, or use profanity. Their occasional brushes with Protestant churches left no imprint on my two brothers, two sisters, or myself. In my family there were never any raised voices, giving the impression that families never had conflict. One of the reasons to go away to college is to discover that none of these things are true in the wider world.

My parents had lived in the Seattle area since I was fourteen, surrounded by the thick green of Douglas Fir forests, the pebbled beaches of Puget Sound, and the mulched rhododendron gardens of our suburban neighborhood. The college town of Pullman, squeezed against the border of Washington and Idaho, was completely different, and the drive to Washington State University made it clear that my terrain was about to change.

The journey from Seattle to Pullman takes six hours by car; for the first hour-and-a-half Interstate 90 rises up thru densely forested mountains to Snoqualmie Pass at the crest of the Cascade Mountains. Immediately after crossing the summit, the change is dramatic. The western slope of the mountains wrings all the moisture from the clouds that come in from the Pacific, depriving the eastern half of the state of precipitation and creating a high desert. As the eastern slope of the Cascades fades away, scattered Ponderosa Pines give way to sage deserts, punctured by black columns of basalt left by the volcanoes that formed the landscape. The highway drops down thousands of feet to cross the mighty Columbia River, where State Highway 26 branches away towards Pullman. Hours later the land shows signs of agriculture, although an Iowa farmer would hardly recognize it as such. Where the land is flat, irrigation machines roll back and forth over the fields, each apparatus carrying a mile of sprinkler pipe driven by an eight-foot metal wheel to bring water to the arid volcanic soil. Where there is no irrigation the land is dry and brown. Tiny crossroads like

Washtucna and Dusty barely break the monotony of the two-lane highway.

Nearing Pullman, the land is pushed up into the distinctive folds of the Palouse Country, like a loose rug that someone tripped over. It would not be accurate to call these rolling hills; the slopes are steep enough to require creative patterns of ploughing, each furrow following the contour of the hill and threatening to overturn the careless tractor or combine. Farmers of the Palouse seem determined to grow wheat on every inch of their land (most farmhouses have crops planted right up to the house, no acreage wasted on lawn or shade trees), and even the steepest hillsides are tilled and planted.

Driving through the Palouse, I had the unmistakable feeling that everything familiar had been left behind. The terrain was so challenging that the hills couldn't be irrigated, so the crops needed to survive the hot, dry summers and bitterly cold winters on their own. This was dry-land wheat farming, in which the hills were planted with wheat in the fall and the seeds were allowed to lay dormant under the winter snow to sprout and grow as the snow melted in the spring. Harvest time came at the beginning of summer, but even then, the fields were stingy with their yields. Never could one see amber waves of grain.

Nearing Pullman, the stark hills always seem either brown and freshly plowed or crusted with several inches of snow. The weather was as forbidding as the landscape, resisting the visitor's approach with icy blasts of sleet or snow blowing sideways, as if to demand "Why are you here?" There was no doubt that I was entering a different world.

During my first years at college, living in a male-only dormitory seemed like a stable and protected environment, with rules and curfews, three meals a day in the nearby co-ed dining hall, and studious surroundings. But these first years spent in Waller Hall were nothing like living at home.

The dorm where I spent my first years of college was one of the oldest student housing buildings, an aging four-story brick building with no elevator. My small room in Fourth North was initially shared with several other freshmen, but they quickly dropped out or moved on, leaving me alone in the space. Most of the rest of the fourth floor was taken up by older students. Sinkey and Dooney (nobody knew their first names) were veterans who had been in college for years on the GI bill, and their home was the large corner room. Both been fixtures on Fourth North since before anyone remembered, and they showed no sign of leaving. Dooney was studying some sort of biology, and he had constructed a series of cages in which he raised quail on the ledge outside his window. Inside his room he kept a variety of reptiles, and the superintendent of the dorm knew that it wasn't worth the effort to try and enforce the "no pets" rule. Sinkey gave no sign of academic effort; he was mainly in charge of the nightly bull sessions on the floor, where younger students were tolerated (as long as they didn't speak).

Since I was a pre-veterinary student, I was particularly fascinated by Harry "The Gross" Disney, who was in his final year of veterinary school. Harry was a not-too-distant relative of Walt Disney, but definitely an R-rated member of the family. He came from the tiny town of Ekalaka, Montana, and would soon be a rural large animal vet in ranch country, where his lack of polish would be right at home. He had earned the nickname of "The Gross" when someone bet him that he wouldn't eat a live goldfish; after he had swallowed a half-dozen medium size fish from Dooney's aquarium, the only person in the room who wasn't queasy was Harry. He also played the banjo and had an extensive repertoire of off-color country songs. Veterinary medicine, it seemed, was an earthy affair.

Harry, Sinkey, and Dooney had lived on Waller Fourth North with other older students for several years with only the occasional naive underclassman. Even the superintendent of the dorm pretty much left our floor alone, possibly because of the rough reputation of the group that became known as the "Dirty Dozen". They had developed their own vigilante system to keep freshmen in line. The simplest of these was the dorm's version of college hazing: The Shower Party. If you were studying in your room and four or five upperclassmen appeared at your door, you could bet that you would be dragged off (putting up a good fight was considered a plus) and thrown into the showers fully clothed. Good clean fun. But many of the activities on Fourth North rose above the level of college pranks.

A series of tasteless practical jokes culminated in my first roommate Brad stealing the door off the hinges of Billy "Bear" Thomas' room and hiding it. The following evening Brad was the recipient of a Mattress Ride: At midnight four of the aggrieved men invaded our room, stripped Brad naked, painted his genitals with Methylene Blue dye from the biology lab, rolled him up in his own mattress, and drove him a mile outside of town, where they left him, mattress and all, in the middle of a wheat field. This got the attention of the dormitory supervisors, but nobody took credit for the act and no retribution was enacted. This was not the academic college life that I had envisioned, and I adopted the defensive strategy of a prairie dog, poking my head out of my room only when I needed to assess the threat level of activities that I heard in the hallway.

What put the Dirty Dozen far above reasonable college pranks was an episode that had happened the spring before I came to Waller Hall. The neighboring dorm, Stinson Hall, was also an old brick building of four stories and no elevator, built at the same time as Waller. For some reason there was bad blood between the older students on Waller Fourth North and the residents of Stinson North.   It had escalated beyond the bounds of decent fun, culminating at Spring Break.   Harry The Gross had access to an ancient horse which had served as a "palpator horse" at the vet school.   It was unhealthy and had outlived its educational usefulness so it was scheduled to be euthanized.   On the first day of Spring Break, Harry and the Dirty Dozen walked the condemned horse out of the large animal barn at the vet school and up the four flights of stairs to the top floor of Stinson Hall.   The residents of that dorm had already departed for vacation, so the Dirty Dozen led the old horse into one of the students' empty rooms and humanely euthanized it with a drugs borrowed from the vet school.   And they left the dead horse in the room to decompose over the week-long break.   I was not present for this legendary episode (and the perpetrators were never identified, except within the private hallway of Waller Fourth North), but the message was clear to every student: Don't mess with Fourth North.

As an anxious underclassman, these episodes were alarming.   I had my Shower Party, but otherwise stayed quietly under the radar.

Living closely with other males of my species was fascinating, if unnerving, and many times it seemed that I might as well be observing strange creatures in a biology field study.   Part of this was cultural; many students in the dorm came from farm backgrounds, while others were from the affluent suburbs of Seattle.   One of my first roommates came from San Diego, where he had grown up with a father who was a member of the radically conservative John Birch Society; predictably, that roommate soon became a reckless rebel who flaunted every one of his father's rules and values.   There were older ex-military students using the benefits of the GI bill, football players whose worth rested on their speed in the 40 yard dash, artsy music and English majors, and aimless eighteen-year-olds who only seemed to be at the university because they couldn't think of anything else to do. There were two students on our floor who must have been gay, and even though one of them was a flamboyant design major and the other a nursing student, I don't remember any rumors about their sexuality, and the other dorm residents hardly took notice of their differences. It seemed that we were all different enough. Even the students whose backgrounds were similar to my own seemed as foreign to me as if they had been from a lost tribe.

The most obvious thing that set me apart from everyone else was alcohol. My own parents never drank, not out of religion or prudery, just good Midwestern caution and a limited social life. If I had any friends in high school I suppose that I might have been at parties where alcohol was involved, but by the time that I entered college I had never actually seen anyone take an alcoholic drink. There was no reason to drink in order to fit in, since I knew that an alcohol-impaired version of myself would not be an improvement.

But at Washington State University it was impossible not to be exposed to rampant intoxication. WSU had the reputation of having the highest alcohol consumption of any college in the country, driven by the boredom and isolation of being in a small town in the middle of nowhere with nothing to do. On weekends it appeared that I was the only sober person in our dorm, possibly on the whole campus. I watched the behavior of my fellow students with a certain puzzled amusement, as if I was observing inexplicable pagan rituals. Strangely, it didn't bother me to live in this beer-soaked environment; I wasn't involved, and they left me alone.

It was the 1960's and there was also rampant drug use, but in the dorm it was kept behind closed doors, as drug use could lead to arrest and expulsion. I had to avoid any proximity to illicit drugs, as I knew that I would have to have a squeaky-clean record in order to get the DEA Controlled Substance license that I would need as a veterinarian.

Studying was my refuge, and there was plenty of it. The pre-veterinary curriculum was the same as pre-medicine; biology, chemistry, physics, bacteriology, nutrition, psychology. I took half again the recommended number of credit hours, hoping to be accepted into the veterinary school as quickly as possible. Only one distraction interrupted my studies.

5

Soul in The Palouse

The whole place smelled like beer. Well, beer and sawdust, with faint afternotes of pepperoni and pizza dough. From a stage at the rear of a long room a band was cranking out soul music, the black lead singer on his knees belting out Sam Cooke's "A Change Is Gonna Come." After the soul ballad was finished a bearded young guitarist, playing a classic Gibson 175 sunburst hollow-body guitar, launched into James Brown's "It's Your Thing" and the dance floor filled as sax, trumpet, and trombone set up a driving riff behind the singer, who was sweating like the Godfather of Soul himself.

Hearing rhythm-and-blues in a tavern in the Palouse border town of Moscow, Idaho seemed a little out of place; but so did the beer-drinking patrons, none of whom looked old enough to drink legally in Washington. Since Idaho's drinking age was 18, the bars in Moscow catered to WSU students who were willing to drive to another state to party, as well as to the locals from the University of Idaho. The Rathaus Tavern attracted the youngest students, perhaps because it was the first drinking establishment on Highway 270 coming into Moscow.

After the music wound down at 1 AM, the guitarist prodded his bandmates to pack up and leave quickly, since he was a pre-vet student and had an 8AM chemistry lab the next morning.

The one exception to my exclusive interest in veterinary medicine was music. I started guitar lessons on an old Sears

Silvertone archtop at the local music store in Colorado Springs owned by legendary jazz guitarist Johnny Smith. As with academic subjects, I found the guitar easy to learn and quickly learned to play, read music, and understand the harmonic theory behind notes and chords. The first guitar teachers that I had were jazz players, and they were happy to have a student who was more interested in the complex harmonies of jazz than in learning three-chord rock'n'roll, so I became a jazz guitarist. This clearly set me apart from my peers, who were listening to the Beatles, the Rolling Stones, and Jefferson Airplane.

Because there was almost no jazz played on the radio in the late 60s, my listening was confined to a few records by Kenny Burrell and Herbie Hancock and the local "soul radio" station, KTAC. I could hear jazz textures in the R&B tunes of Arethra, Little Stevie Wonder, and the Temptations, and every so often they might play a bluesy jazz tune like Cannonball Adderly's "Mercy Mercy Mercy".

Those musical interests continued into college, but the only place where a jazz guitarist might fit was in the WSU stage band; not a very hip ensemble, but I knew the musical language and was the only guitarist on campus that could actually read music. Rehearsals provided something different to do on Wednesday nights.

When three of the horn players from stage band decided to start a group, they asked me to join, although it was outside my comfort zone. Our first band featured an African American singer in the James Brown mold and an organist who could carry his Lowry organ better than he could carry a tune; both were members of the WSU football squad, but found time for extra-curricular music. We learned enough R&B tunes to play fraternity dances and landed a regular gig at the Rathaus in Moscow. I still had never tasted beer, but I was spending every Friday and Saturday night playing music for drunken fraternity bashes and small-town taverns. Driving back from Moscow at 1 AM after playing a gig was hazardous, since nobody sober was on the road: Several times we had to stop to assist drunks who had driven off the road or turned their car over. Because our audiences were largely small-town white kids, most of them had never heard the R&B songs that we played and many had the impression that we must have written the tunes ourselves. I soon became accustomed to playing loud music in bars and fraternities until the early hours every weekend; it allowed me to use the two nights that I allowed myself to take a break from studies and earn a few dollars. But perhaps scheduling a chemistry lab on Saturday morning wasn't a good idea.

Fraternities often hired us out-of-town parties, which took us to parts of the state that we would otherwise have avoided. When we were booked for a fraternity gig at Whitman College in Walla Walla a blizzard hit the southeast corner of the state and the main highway was closed. We couldn't cancel, so we took an alternative route, winding our way down the treacherous Lewiston Grade at night (a two thousand foot drop of dark snow-covered switchbacks in seven miles) and following the Snake River to our gig. All seven band members had crowded into Johnny Davis' Plymouth Valiant, pulling a rental trailer with our gear behind. We were less frightened of the road conditions than we were of being pulled over by a police officer in one of the small towns along the way; a black guy driving an old car packed with long-haired musicians and a trailer of expensive gear was an invitation to harassment, or worse. We felt a little better when the lone car that passed us only held three nuns.

Playing in a band wasn't the only music that I pursued. As a student I was allowed to take any music classes that the university offered, so I squeezed music theory, class piano, and classical guitar lessons into my schedule. Despite completing the required courses, however, the university refused grant me a minor in music (although I had met all the requirements) when I finally received my veterinary degree. They felt that music was irrelevant to becoming a veterinarian.

6

Fire and Doubt

At the end of the 1960's politics and cultures were clashing everywhere, even in an isolated college town in eastern Washington. The civil rights struggle filled the headlines, occasionally spilling over into our mostly-white university. One of the African-American basketball players had been accused of some minor crime (fairly or unfairly, it was hard to tell in the climate of the times) and a sit-in was held to protest the potentially racist situation. Several students from Waller Hall decided to hang a sign on the footbridge to the administration building over Campus Way that read "WSU: Another Ol' Miss?", referring to a racial incident at a southern university. When they urged me to come along to post the message, I joined them, partly for the sense of late 60's activist adventure. I agreed with the sentiments, although I was unclear about the details of the local case. Several days later, campus police showed up at Waller Hall to apprehend the students that had been identified as posting the sign, including myself, and we were taken to the campus police station for questioning. The officer seemed a bit puzzled; he held up the sign from the bridge and asked us if we had posted it. We confessed, since it didn't seem like a crime. Then the officer asked "What does it mean?" Apparently, our vague answers satisfied him, or else he just didn't know what to do with us, so he let us go, warning against future littering, or posting unauthorized materials, or anything else suspicious or dangerous. I noticed him writing something about the incident in a file and hoped that this minor involvement in civil disobedience wouldn't come back to be a problem.

The mood on campus was distinctly on-edge in 1969. During this time my dorm was the target of a series of small fires that were set in the trash closets, reaching a crisis when a Molotov cocktail (the firebomb of choice in those simpler days) was thrown into the basement corridor of Waller North. Anxiety was stoked when fire alarms went off in the middle of the night several times a week. Then suddenly the fires stopped, with no explanation of the motivation for the incidents.

All of these events painted the backdrop for the most important event in my life thus far: In February I submitted my application for veterinary school. Only one out of ten applicants would be accepted (human medical schools were accepting one in five pre-med students at that time), so I knew that the odds were long.

In my favor was a near-perfect grade-point average and a summer of job experience with a veterinarian. Counting against me was that I had only two years of college experience (most applicants had three or four years, but my three years of credits should have counted for something). My future would be determined by the interview.

At this point there was nothing I could do to prepare for the interview, so I distracted myself by deciding what to wear. I had been told that I should wear a tie with my one nice shirt to impress them with my professionalism, so I bought a tie at The Empire, Pullman's only department store, hoping that it said "I'm serious." But I had never learned to tie one, so on the day of my interview I had to call my dad and he talked me through the process. I was as ready as I would ever be.

Being judged in person is unexpectedly different from anything else you can do. It is the pinnacle of inter-personal interaction, with all of the power sitting on the opposite side of the table. I was apprehensive, but were these thoughts or feelings? My cerebral cortex rationally evaluated my chances and knew that odds were against me, reason enough to worry. But the heart-racing, sweat-inducing feeling of adrenaline was missing, and I thought it strange that I felt no emotional reaction. Was there something wrong with me? I would later notice this same lack of visceral feelings, events when my fight-or-flight nerves should have been on fire but I experienced only detached concern. I eventually came to realize that my muted autonomic response would be useful when a severely injured dog or a cat with a blood clot blocking its aorta needed immediate attention, but it did seem like I was missing the stomach-churning excitement of big events. All I could do was show up to the interview and see what happened.

I walked into a small office to find three professors seated across the table from a wobbly vinyl-covered chair. Dr. C, who looked like he had stepped right out of 1950 with black-rimmed glasses and Brylcreemed hair, appeared to be in charge. I answered the expected questions: "Why do you want to be a veterinarian?", "Are you interested in large or small animals?", "What experience do you have with animals." My answers were predictable, likely the same as every other interviewee. There was a pause as Dr. Cummings looked at my file. "I see that you play in a rock band." I could tell right away that this was not in my favor. He was looking at my beard and collar-length hair with lowered eyebrows. I found myself hoping that my file didn't include any references to my campus police interview after the civil-rights sit in. Then the final question: "What will you do if you are not accepted to veterinary school?" This took me by surprise; I must have looked like an antelope that suddenly runs into a lion; now I could finally feel the wash of adrenaline, sweat running down my back and a heartbeat that must be audible from across the room. I had no other plan. Ever since third grade I was committed to becoming a veterinarian, and I couldn't conceive of any other option. I mumbled something about getting a degree in biology, and suddenly it was clear that the interview was over.

The next six weeks dragged on with no news about my application. Other pre-vet students had received their letters of acceptance in early April, so when I left for spring break without receiving a letter I assumed that I would get a rejection letter later. I spent the vacation week trying to answer the big question: What would I do?

Relief came when I returned to campus after the break and found an acceptance letter in my mailbox.

On the heels of this good news came another crisis. During the 1960s college students were given a 2S "student deferment" from the military draft, as long as they stayed in good academic standing. But with the Vietnam War dragging on more draftees were needed and the student deferment was discontinued. Students were then eligible for the draft, and a lottery was held to determine which unlucky college students would be the first to feel Uncle Sam tap him on the shoulder. The prospect of joining the military didn't bother me as much as the prospect of going to war when I had finally won my spot in veterinary school.

The draft lottery was held on a Wednesday night, with each birthday randomly assigned a draft priority number. The student radio station broadcast the numbers as they were drawn. If your birthday was attached to a number less than 100 you were virtually guaranteed to be drafted, and you might as well forget going to your classes the next day. Any number less than 200 suggested that you should consider enlisting in one of the less hazardous branches of the service, such as the Navy or Coast Guard.

On this particular Wednesday night I had a Stage Band rehearsal, so I asked another student to listen for my birthday and let me know my fate as soon as I returned from practice. After a distracted rehearsal that dragged on forever I returned to my dorm and located the designated student, who was as drunk as everyone else in the dorm that evening. What was my draft number? I asked. He thought he heard that my birthday was assigned the number 35. It seemed that I was headed for IndoChina, not veterinary school, and the certainty that had held my life together vanished.

The next morning I checked the school newspaper for the published list of birthdays and draft numbers. Scanning down the list of numbers, at first I couldn't find my birthday. Finally, there it was: Number 352. The army would not get to me until they had exhausted most of our country's other young men in the futile war effort. The last obstacles to reaching veterinary school disappeared and a comforting certainty settled in.

In a blur the semester was over, and I moved in with my parents for the summer recess, returning to my job as kennel help at a local veterinary clinic. I fed dogs and administered flea baths. The cat cages were cleaned twice a day and lined with fresh newspaper and clean cat pans. I quickly learned how to sense when a nervous cat was too stressed and I learned the body language of dogs that required careful handling: The fear biter, the you-can't-do'that-to-me nipper, and the make-my-day "land shark". I acquired "poodle wrangling" skills with a leash and folded towel that would eventually prove invaluable.

One of the most common duties of my job was worming dogs for intestinal parasites. Intestinal worms were diagnosed with a "fecal floatation": Roundworms, hookworms, whipworms and strongyloid worms each produce characteristic microscopic eggs, which were identified by mixing a scoop of fresh feces with a saturated sugar solution and leaving it to float in a test tube overnight. The parasite eggs are lighter than the sugar solution, so they float up and stick to a microscope slide atop the tube. Each night we had a dozen fecal floatations running, kept in a tiny closet-sized room to isolate the smell from the rest of the clinic. After the first month, my boss let me read the tests, an interesting, if smelly, introduction to the science of laboratory diagnosis. Once the type of worm was identified an appropriate medication was prescribed, and it was my job to administer the huge pills (for a large dog the capsule might be two inches long) and wait for the results as the dog rested in one of our concrete runs. The medications were so harsh that the dog required an enema if the worms were not passed (along with foul-smelling diarrhea) within a few hours. The most common parasites were roundworms, present in 70% of puppies, and they would pass as a wiggling mass resembling spaghetti, accompanied by the chemical smell of the medication, which smelled like the glue used to assemble model airplanes (toluene). The dogs always looked happy and relieved when I reunited them with their owners.

I had not yet studied infectious diseases in school, but I certainly knew about rabies. In most mammals the typical signs of rabies (drooling, difficulty swallowing, and seizures) develop within four weeks of exposure, and anyone exposed to the animal within the two weeks preceding symptoms is at risk for contracting rabies. Skunks are an exception and may not develop symptoms for six months, making the rabies-exposed skunk a viral time-bomb. The disease is always fatal once symptoms occur, in both people and other animals.

During this summer we had such a patient quarantined at the clinic. The skunk had been purchased in Portland and one of its littermates had recently been diagnosed with rabies. Rather than have their new pet euthanized, the owners chose to quarantine the pet skunk at our clinic until the authorities decided that no one would be in danger. No one would be in danger except me, that is.

The skunk spent the entire summer at the hospital. At first the little black-and-white animal would stamp his feet and show me his teeth while I edged a bowl of food into the cage and retrieved that litter pan for cleaning, but both of us relaxed as the weeks passed. I said hello to my guest each morning when I came in and gave him food and water, and I served him dinner and said goodnight just before I left each night. My boarder never developed symptoms, and we parted ways when I left for school in September. I never learned what happened to him but I wished him well as I made the transition from regular college student to veterinary school freshman.

7

Companions

As I picked myself up out of the manure trough behind the tail end of a palpator cow, I pondered, for just a moment, the bizarre situation in which I found myself. I had been accepted to veterinary school because I was good at memorizing lecture notes and taking tests, not so much for hands-on (or hands-inside, as it were) proficiency. Then I realized that I had now learned three things: that the inside anatomy of a cow is hard to describe, that cows can kick in any direction they choose, and that being a vet required much more than book learning.

I shared a lab table and cadavers with three other students. Forming dissecting teams had been like kids choosing up sides for baseball; we were the only ones still standing after the large animal guys formed their groups, the handful of women in our class joined together, and the more experienced small animal first-years had found their cliques. Looking around, we were the only ones left.

Mike B was an intense student of Greek ancestry, with wild jet-black hair, dark eyes, and a serious case of test anxiety. Leroy D was calm and self-assured, slightly built, with fine light-brown hair and a casual smile. He was a little older than the rest of our group, and married. Leroy had a background in the dog show world, which translated into a better summer job than the rest of us, who were lucky to be cleaning kennels for our hometown vets from June to August. Bespectacled Timothy O was my own age, but his prevet classes had been taken at a community college, and making the leap into the difficult work of vet school was challenging. He barely managed to survive academically through the first year, but gradually found his footing, and by our third year he was an A student. Tim was quiet and didn't talk much in lab, but neither did the rest of us; conversation consisted of grunts and short questions: "Can you find the medial saphenous vein?" or "This dog is missing the phrenic nerve."

An observer might mistake our dissection group for a band of stone-age hunters huddled around a deer carcass, or perhaps a pride of lions dismantling a wildebeest. Except for the ties, the white lab coats, and the arcane vocabulary involved, the scenarios had certain similarities.

Our year of anatomy explored all of the internal organs, the skeleton and the muscles that moved it, and the pumps and vessels that carried oxygen, nutrients, and hormones to the tissues. Fully half our efforts were focused on the nervous system, including the brain, the spine, and the tiny white strands of the nerves themselves. Each nerve that we located in the paw could be traced up the leg, joining other nerves in bundles that extended into the spinal cord. Within the spinal cord, we traced the neurons as they ran in tracts toward the collection of myelinated cells in the brain. The wiring diagram of an office building would have been much simpler to decipher, and by the time we reached the dog's brain our own brains had run out of storage capacity. Our understanding of how information flows thru the brainstem, medulla, cerebellum, amygdala, hippocampus, and all the various parts of the cortex was less than complete. The one thing I found remarkable (besides the incredible complexity) was the appearance of nerve tissue. Most other tissues were squishy or spongy, and even in our preserved cadaver the pinkness of most tissue suggested cells fed by blood. But even though the brain receives more blood flow than any other part of the body, the tissue is bone-white, with texture that suggested tissue held together by fine filaments. Flow of information is imprinted into the nature of the brain, form following function.

The emergence of consciousness, emotion, and behavior from the strands of nerve tissue is a mystery that humans have pondered and argued over for centuries, ever since the second century, when Galen established that the brain, not the heart, is the seat of intelligence and emotion. Our exploration of the nervous system told us nothing about the behaviors that our dog Fred showed in life. I could not find where bounding joy at his owner's attention arose, or where his anguish at becoming a homeless stray in the dog pound was located. I couldn't see it.

Animal behavior had been an interest of mine since childhood, but at no point in veterinary school was the subject of behavior taught. We were never told why a horse would lay its ears back against his head in annoyance, or why a dog might cock his head when talked to.

We were taught to control our patients, but never to understand them. I learned a little something about the mysteries of the animal mind from my roommate during my freshman year.

A small single room on the 4th floor of Waller Hall had been my home for two years, and even though it was against the rules I adopted a kitten to keep me company. The kitten had been found abandoned and brought to the clinic where I worked during the summer. She was barely 4 weeks old and still needed bottle feeding when I started my first year of vet school, so I brought her with me and raised her in my dorm room. She was gray with faint tabby stripes and a few peculiar habits.

I didn't give my kitten a name. In my youthful animal-centered thinking I felt that any name would be superfluous, and it was unnecessary to burden an animal by labelling it with a human word. She was simply my cat; she was who she was. What she was, however, was a little peculiar. I would later learn that all cats invent their own behaviors, that they are social in their own aloof, observant ways, and that they understand, not obey.

When I was in my room studying, the kitten was on my lap constantly, curled up or kneading my legs with her paws. Frequently she would suck on the buttons of my shirt, leaving my shirt wet and eventually pulling the buttons loose. Soon none of my clothes had any buttons. It was evident that this "oral fixation" was likely a result of not being allowed to nurse on her mother until the normal weaning age of six weeks. If she had been a person perhaps she would have developed a nervous habit of chewing her nails or smoking cigarettes. She never outgrew this obsession, so I accepted it and learned how to sew on buttons.

Harder to tolerate was her habit of sitting on the stereo turntable as my records played. My copy of John Coltrane Live at The Village Vanguard still bears the scratches from the needle skittering across vinyl when she hopped on the turntable for a ride.

She clearly knew that her behavior was against the rules. She would not do it until I sat down at my desk across the room, but as soon as I was seated where I couldn't reach her she would stroll casually onto the spinning record and I would leap up and chase her off. She would wait until I sat down again and repeat the trick. She definitely did it for my reaction; if I stepped out of the room while a record was playing, I never heard the music skip a beat from the hallway. As soon as I came back into my room and sat down, the behavior would occur on cue. It was obvious that this was an attempt to elicit a reaction; whether she found it humorous in her feline way or was simply being perverse in trying to claim her role in our relationship, I couldn't tell, but she taught me that most animal behaviors are conscious and intentional, not mere automatic instinctive responses. She shared my room throughout my first vet school year, but disappeared during the end-of-year car trip to Seattle. She was an outgoing and affectionate companion, and I knew that she would find herself a new home and invent some new behaviors to go with it, while my home would remain in the Palouse.

Washington State University was built on a hill overlooking the town of Pullman. Thousands of students studying education, communications, English, and chemistry trudged up the steep sidewalks on their way to classes. The School of Veterinary Medicine occupied two plain buildings at the bottom of the hill, isolated from the traffic of regular university life.

Lecture classes were held in Wegner Hall, a plain two-story brick structure, while McCoy Hall sprawled along the other edge of a grassy triangle, two rectangular stories of modern concrete spaced with windows. Anatomy and surgery labs occupied McCoy, along with the teaching hospital, examination rooms, surgery suites, radiology facilities, and wards housing dog and cat patients. At night a strange purple glow emanated from the high windows in McCoy Hall, creating a spooky mystery that wasn't explained until my third year.

Just adjacent to McCoy Hall were the cement corridors and box stalls of barns A, B, and C of the large animal hospital. Hidden behind these two buildings were a variety of barns and outbuildings where a number of teaching and research animals lived. In one old-style whitewashed barn a motley population of farm animals idled about with no apparent purpose. A couple of sheep wandered about in one pen, the palpator cows from anatomy spent their off-duty hours chewing cud, and inexplicably a single black bear paced in an enclosure at the back of the barn. In the rear parking lot sat a small windowless building where ducks and chickens were kept in a light-controlled environment, allowing poultry researchers to mess with their photoperiods and study the effects of artificially shortened day/night cycles, six hours of day followed by six hours of night. The veterinary school was Old MacDonald-meets-Alice in Wonderland, my home for four years of vet school. A place where unexpected things were possible.

Interlude 1

I had never seen anyone put ketchup on cottage cheese and I was curious. I was fascinated by the petite blonde at the end of the lunch table, but we never really met. Since Waller Hall had no dining facility, the Waller residents had to eat all of their meals in the cafeteria of Stevenson Hall, a nearby women's dorm with three modern towers. At each meal time the young men of Waller Hall would walk down the hill to the Stevenson dining hall, where students would line up at long tables with their plates of food, white porcelain cups of dining-hall coffee, and their friends. Sitting at a table with other Waller residents I couldn't help notice the girl with a cheerful personality and shoulder-length blonde hair, curled at the end in the style of the day (when women slept with rollers in their hair). At first I would just listen in on conversations between this girl, her roommate, and my dorm-mates, and enjoy being at the edge of her small social group. Her name was Terri.

I was strongly attracted but saw no likelihood that she was similarly afflicted. I fantasized that I might ask her for a walk or a cup of coffee at the Student Union Building, but when our band played for an overnight out-of-town fraternity function in Worley, Idaho (what kind of frat would hold a weekend party at a motel in Worley, I wondered), Terri showed up at the event with one of the fraternity members. At an overnight party. So much for that fantasy.

But eventually the time came for Thanksgiving break, and students were looking for rides home to Western Washington for the holiday. During the previous summer I had convinced my parents to buy me a car, with the excuse that I needed transportation for my musical gear when our band played a gig. My first vehicle was a model of unreliability, an old turquoise Greenbrier van that Chevrolet had manufactured for a few dark years. The van featured lots of room inside, but it was powered by the same four-cylinder air-cooled engine that underpowered the compact Chevy Corvair. The van would get from here to there, but not with speed or reliability. It seemed the perfect vehicle with which to impress a young woman, so when dinner-table talk turned to how people were getting home for Thanksgiving I nonchalantly mentioned that I could give Terri a ride to the other side of the mountains if she wanted. Which she did. Her parents lived in Bellevue, a mere 5 miles south of my parents' house in Kirkland, so I could excuse the boldness of my offer by claiming that, after all, her house was right on my way. As plans go, this seemed to be going well.

Terri had gratefully accepted my offer of a ride, but somehow one of the musicians in our band also managed to invite himself along. John O also lived in Bellevue, so it was hard to refuse him a ride. John was a talented piano player, but his ego was even greater than his keyboard abilities, and when our road trip finally took place John talked (mostly about himself) for entire the six hour trip. Now my plan to get to know Terri better seemed doomed. The return trip to Pullman a week later was no better. The best I could hope was that Terri would appreciate the transportation. I couldn't tell whether she was favorably inclined toward me, but when I reminded her that Christmas break was only three weeks away, she accepted that ride offer as well. I took it as a good sign.

Three weeks passed, and I fabricated an excuse to keep anyone else from coming along on our drive to Seattle for Christmas Break. Finally, I had the chance to be alone with Terri.

In between long periods of silence we shared our life stories. Terri had been born in Alaska, where her father (now an airline pilot, but then a struggling aircraft mechanic) had built a cabin on a homestead on the Kenai Peninsula.. This bit of history was more adventurous than I would have expected from her. After living at the isolated homestead cabin with her mother, brother, and sister for several years (her father was away working in Anchorage for long periods) and watching for bears and moose as she and her brother carried buckets of water up from Lake Longmere to heat on the wood stove, the family eventually moved into Anchorage, where they stayed with a succession of other families.

For a few years her family was stationed in Bethel, an Eskimo village where her family were the only white residents. Terri's father plied his aircraft mechanic trade until he completed his pilot rating and started flying for Alaska Airlines, and moved to Seattle when the airlines relocated its headquarters. Terri denied having an adventurous childhood, claiming they were "just kids", but somehow my own story seemed pathetically tame by comparison.

For our trip Terri had brought a metal tin filled with chocolate chip cookies that she had made for the trip, which I took as an encouraging sign; isn't sharing food a sign of interest? We snacked on the cookies most of the way across the state.

After driving across the interminable sagebrush of central Washington, we sped up the dry east side of Snoqualmie Pass to the crest of the Cascade Mountains. The summit is only 3200 feet above sea level, but the weather changes abruptly as coastal clouds release their precipitation on the west side of the pass. The change was almost instantaneous: One moment we were traveling uphill at 60 mph on a dry road, the next moment we were on a steep downhill lined with ten foot snowbanks and frosted with a sheet of ice. Immediately the van started to skid, spinning slowly in a full circle down the steep west side of the pass. Fortunately, there were no other cars on the road as the van completed a full slow-motion rotation before coming to rest with its nose deep in the snowbank on the left side of the highway. Our mood changed from pleasant journey, to panic, to now-what-are-we-going-to-do? in less than a minute.

The van was stuck, and I couldn't back it out of the snowbank. Terri handed me the empty cookie tin: "Will this help?" Sometimes a ridiculous idea becomes inventive brilliance when there isn't another option.

The cookie tin served as a reasonable substitute for a shovel, and after 20 minutes I had excavated the hood of the van enough to free it and back out of the snow. We didn't talk much on the rest of the trip.

After returning to Pullman after Christmas I made another attempt to impress her with transportation. As part of her third year requirements for an education degree she had to assist in an elementary school classroom for a week. The school was across town and up a steep hill. Winter had set in, and to spare her the two mile walk in the blowing cold I offered to drive her to school every day before I went to class. She accepted my offer, but this trip also came to a bad end. The brief ride across town was fine, but when I turned up the hill the van coughed and groaned, unable to climb the hill at all. Reluctantly I told Terri that I was sorry, but she would have to get out and walk the last mile up the hill. The rest of the week she walked herself to school. She seemed to forgive the inconvenience, and encouraged by her incomprehensible tolerance for my unreliable transportation, I asked her for a real date and a new adventure began.

Much later I asked Terri what she had seen in me and why she still showed interest. She admits that there was an element of rebellion involved. At the time I had shoulder-length hair, a wide-brimmed black hat, and I played in a rock band. When I met her parents they were a little shocked that their well-behaved daughter would go out with someone like me. But maybe the "future doctor" label helped.

Winter in the Palouse was cold and windy, and lasted until the end of April. It seemed that Terri had become my girlfriend (although I don't remember referring to her in that way at the time), and that meant we spent a lot of time walking—down into the little town of Pullman, out along Farm Way to see the deer farm and the experimental apple orchards, and up College Hill to the campus art gallery (not because we knew anything about paintings or photography, but because it was freezing outside and the gallery was warm and free). When we returned to Terri's dormitory we stood outside for a long as we could stand the cold, since male students were not allowed in the women's dorms. It was hard to say goodnight, but we could only stand the chill for so long and there was still studying to be done, no matter what the hour. Anatomy and physiology always called, claiming what was left of me.

8

How Things Work

Anatomy was real, visceral, tangible. Something that could be seen, felt, and understood in a mechanical way. Muscles and tendons provide leverage on the skeleton in a manner that makes locomotion possible. The four chambers of the heart look like a pump, with valves directing flow to eject fluid in the desired direction. Even that least prestigious section of anatomy, the digestive tract, makes it clear how food is turned into feces: kibble or hay goes down this tube, pauses in several holding areas to reduce it into nutrients, and the leftovers leave thru a tube in the other end. Anatomy is simple, visual. But anatomy is for surgeons, those laborers who take things apart and put them back together. The actual processes of life take place at an unseen level: enzymes, proteins, chemicals, genes—the domain of physiology.

Physiology satisfied my need to understand things. I had always been fascinated by how things work; not radios or internal combustion engines, but flesh, blood, and brain things. Learning about life in molecular and cellular detail explained so much about animals at the organism level and it only takes a few steps down this path to realize that everything—everything—is more complicated than it seems on the surface. Complicated, but not impossible to understand.

For first year veterinary students the afternoons were dedicated to the hands-on learning of anatomy, but mornings were claimed by subjects that revealed life at the most basic levels:

Histology (the study of cells), Immunology (the study of self and non-self), Endocrinology (everything is run by hormones), and even Biophysics (everything that isn't run by hormones is run by electricity or hydrodynamics). The interactions of chemistry, enzymes. electrolytes, and proteins became a crossword puzzle to solve, piece by piece.

Knowing how things work provides a feeling of control, and a world that makes sense down to its finest details is reassuring. From the basic elements one can climb the ladder of complexity to understand the world. From genes, proteins are produced by lining up the right amino acids. From proteins, hormones and regulatory peptides are produced. From hormones, the body functions are kept in harmony. From this balance, emotions and cognition are generated ("Feelings are the mental expression of homeostasis", as Antonio Damasio puts it). Ultimately one might even understand humans, their feelings and behaviors.

Each beat of the heart is a composition more intricate than a Mozart symphony: Information from DNA in the chromosomes builds heart cells, which are only slightly different than the cells in the muscles that move us. Each muscle cell has channels that allow calcium ions to flow across its surface membrane, causing fibers of myosin to shorten. Heart muscle doesn't just contract on its own: The nerves in the atrial pacemaker fire electrical impulses at regular intervals, contracting the upper chambers of the heart, but also relaying the message to the atrioventricular node, triggering the powerful muscles of the ventricles to pump blood to the body. All of these coordinated functions are adjusted by adrenaline in the bloodstream and by the vagus nerve, the "wandering nerve" that carries messages back and forth from the internal organs. And every one of these functions can be broken down into even smaller details. Each cellular action must make its entrance in precise measure at exactly the right time to synchronize with the functions of other cells to create the music of life.

Learning the secrets of physiology indelibly changed my view of life. Now a minor intestinal upset was no longer just a pain in the gut; I could now picture the intense pressure of peristaltic waves coursing through the smooth muscle layers of the colon to create the unpleasant sensation. Hunger was not just a desire for food, but a combination of my blood sugar level, the sensation of glands secreting in the stomach lining, and the longings of chemical receptors in the olfactory epithelium and taste buds.

Even brain cells, masters of the nervous system and signifiers of our hopes, dreams, wants, and desires, could be described in microscopic detail, with infinitesimal electrical impulses releasing neurotransmitting chemicals that trigger more infinitesimal electrical impulses in neighboring neurons. Our very thoughts and behaviors can be expressed in neuroendocrine terms, suggesting the question of "Who are we?". From this perspective we might feel like occupants of a small boat riding the tide of a living ocean, barely in control, but in the end our physiology is who we are.

Philosophers (and many "holistic" medical practitioners) mistrust reductionism, insisting that the whole of a complex system like a dog or a horse is greater than the sum of its tiny parts, and an animal is somehow different in its entirely than in its component elements. Medicine could be practiced as if the body was a black box, matching symptoms to treatments without considering underlying details, but this approach is naively incomplete.

A vomiting patient might benefit from anti-emetic medication to control the symptoms, but physiology instructs us to imagine all of the different parts of the body that might be involved when Fido retches and leaves his dinner on the living room floor. Direct irritation of the stomach will certainly trigger the vomiting reflex, but so will stimulation of the inner ear by infection or by the Vestibular Syndrome that is commonly seen in aged dogs. Throwing up is commonly caused not by the stomach itself, but by some foreign chemical in the bloodstream sensed by the "chemoreceptor trigger zone", a tiny cluster of neurons in the brain which senses food toxins, waste products that accumulate with kidney failure, or alcohol (the most frequent offender in humans). Sometimes vomiting is all in the brain, and a stomach coating medicine or antacid is of no use. The details of physiology are important.

The philosophical argument against reducing life to its individual details is that in some way it reduces the specialness of life, replacing mystery and magic with chemistry and chromosomes. But personally I felt enriched by knowing about the many layers and connections that made me.

By the end of my first year in veterinary school I had little contact with living animals (except the cranky Holsteins in large animal anatomy lab), but I had gained a great appreciation for the intricacies of the living organism. The pieces fit together like parts in an orchestra, each system complimenting the other in ever-changing harmonies. Soon enough I would enter my second year, and find how everything can go terribly wrong.

9

Things Gone Terribly Wrong

After a year spent learning how the body was arranged and functioned, I had gained an appreciation for the marvelous complexity of the living organism. Anatomy and physiology paint a picture of the animal as a perfect creature, driven by the harmony of homeostasis; all is right in the physiologic world. Until things go terribly wrong.

Then comes Pathology, the troublesome stepchild of Anatomy and Physiology, the story of how the body's perfect machinery can leave the rails and crash into a pile of rubble.

Dissecting cadavers in year one was followed in year two by endless days in pathology lab and lectures learning about the many ways that life can be broken. The pathology laboratory was an opportunity to see and feel tissues that had failed, destroyed by infection, toxins, cancer, or a dozen other obscure causes, while the lecture hours were filled with explanations of how those bad things could happen. Just so that we didn't forget the long list of diseases that could affect each tissue, we were taught the mnemonic of DAMNIT: Any condition could be Degenerative, Developmental, Allergic, Autoimmune, Metabolic, Mechanical, Nutritional, Neoplastic (cancer), Inflammatory, Immune-mediated, Iatrogenic (caused by the doctor), Ischemic (caused by lack of blood supply), Idiopathic (with causes that we don't know, because even doctors can be idiots), Toxic, or Traumatic.

For every beautiful organ, neatly organized in sheets of perfect, uniform cells, there are a dozen kinds of ugly. The normal intestine with its cream-colored smooth muscle, a pearly serosal surface on the outside and an even granular mucosal surface on the inside, might turn puffy and swollen, or bloody red on the inside, or speckled with tiny bruises on the outside, or lumpy with tumors, or purple and necrotic from obstruction, or thin and atrophied from lack of food. Or sometimes all of these things together. Even the normal appearing intestine might reveal disease under the microscope, with infiltrates of white blood cells or clumps of cancerous lymphocytes (which are often so similar to normal lymph cells that even the microscope often can't distinguish them). Careful examination might detect a lack of the fine nerve fibers needed to drive the muscular contractions of peristalsis that move the journey from food to feces. The lists of bad things that can happen to cells and organs seemed endless, echoing Leo Tolstoy's observation that "Happy families are alike; every unhappy family is unhappy in its own way". The countless aberrations of anatomy and physiology created an impossible mass of knowledge to memorize and absorb.

Pathology lectures were filled with a bewildering load of novel vocabulary and detailed explanation, accompanied by pictures. The typical case might start out with a blurry slide projected on the screen of a nondescript brown dog in a poorly lit hallway. "As you can see, this dog is showing a lack of abdominal muscle tone" (What? Where?). "And here is a list of diseases that could cause this pot-bellied appearance", at which point the professor would flash a slide for three seconds showing a list of ten conditions with long scientific names. As we raced to record these diseases in our notes he would move on to a slide showing tissue sections of muscle, intestine, and adrenal gland from the now-deceased patient, each microscopic picture a mosaic of pink and purple-stained cells. The DNA in the nucleus of each cell absorbs the purple hematoxyin stain—Does the nucleus look a little pale and granular? Tiny granules in the body of the cells take up the pink eosin dye, happy little pink polka dots. Maybe there is an immune reaction triggered by a parasite or an allergen? The lists of diseases and microscopic slides seemed as arcane and mysterious as if they had come from an ancient book of sorcery. A brief pause, and then another dozen slides illustrating a different example of biology behaving badly.

If lectures were densely packed with testable information organized by body system, pathology lab was an entirely different experience. Path Lab explored tissues from whatever unfortunate animal had died and been sent to the school's post mortem department, what was casually referred to as "going to necropsy". After the clinical pathologists performed their necropsy on a cow with a fibrotic liver or a still-born lamb, they saved the good parts for the pathology students. Every morning at 8AM stainless steel carts loaded with diseased body parts were wheeled into the lab for inspection. The tissues were slippery and smelled organic and fleshy, like cream-of-wheat mixed with blood. Samples of infected lymph nodes or crimson muscle tissue were placed on metal trays, disease served cafeteria-style.

The masters-of-ceremony for our daily mayhem-and-mortality show competed to discuss what each tissue revealed about the cause of death. Dr. Dickenson was 6'4", an intimidating ex-Marine with a greying crewcut and no sense of humor. Dr. Henson was of medium build and academic appearance, with glasses, hair neatly parted and combed and, well, no sense of humor.

Dr D would lift the four-pound heart of a cow that had been sick for a month before it died and was trucked to the vet school to determine if it had died from some contagious disease. The left side of the heart was clearly abnormal, with a sickly yellow patch three inches across, standing in sharp contrast to the maroon surface of the normal heart muscle. A lengthy argument would ensue, with Dr D describing how this cow could have died of a nutritional problem that had resulted in a deficiency of Vitamin E and the trace element selenium, causing muscle damage that sent the bovine into heart failure. Dr H would interrupt, refuting Dr D's explanation. Look at the scar on the reticulum, the second stomach with its network of ridges, he would argue: Clearly some metal object like a nail had become trapped in the reticulum and worked its way thru the stomach wall, gradually migrating forward through the liver and into the surface of the heart, causing an inflamed area of heart muscle (apparently a common barnyard condition with the sensible and descriptive name of Hardware Disease). It was obvious, insisted Dr H; the only evidence that was missing was the nail to prove it. But you don't have the nail, do you? Dr D would shoot back. An infection of the lungs could have spread thru the bloodstream. finding its way to the heart muscle and causing an infection that caused the heart damage. Dr D would ask if the lungs had been sent up with the rest of the organs, which they hadn't. Dr H would insist that the lungs would not have shown much, but Dr D would raise his drill-sergeant voice and bark that it was inexcusable: How can anyone expect him to diagnose the cause of death without all of the tissues?

Dr D and Dr H would argue for most of an hour over a single set of specimens, ignoring the students as we sat at our lab tables waiting to examine the tissues. Eventually someone would ask the only question that we cared about: Why did the cow die? Without looking at each other, both doctors would nod and state with authority that the cow had obviously died of heart failure.

Most of the samples that made it to the path lab were from farm animals; no cats ever donated their organs for our inspection, and it was a rare treat for the small animal students when a deceased dog made its way across the necropsy table. The pets that were referred to the veterinary school were the most difficult cases, often hopeless, with owners willing to exhaust every ray of hope and drive hundreds of miles to try and save their dog. Those cases were thoroughly worked up; there was rarely any question of cause-of-death, and very few distraught owners would authorize a post-mortem.

But farmers and ranchers had urgent financial interests in their stock; an undiagnosed case of Hoof-And-Mouth Disease or Bovine Respiratory Disease could decimate their herd, and every livestock death demanded an explanation. While Dr. D and Dr. H. argued about the details of demise, the farmer was just happy to know that the rest of his herd was safe from contagious disease.

Each day the same scenario would be replayed. Every case was different, but the uncertainties of the end-of-life marched across our tables in a constant procession. No mention was ever made of what could have been done to save these patients, giving the impression that life was fragile and our ability to alter the course of disease was limited. No one gets out alive.

10

Guinevere

After three years in Waller Hall I had moved out to a shabby attic apartment with a roommate. Ken C was a tall red-headed General Studies major my own age with freckles and a broad smile that made him look like Howdy Doody, and he spoke in a slang that was all his own. He played drums in our band with infectious enthusiasm and the band's other percussionist lived just downstairs, creating an environment not suitable for study. Ken's slovenliness was legendary; the rooms came with a month's supply of dishes, and once those were dirty they stayed unwashed in the sink for the remainder of our year in the apartment.

The only other resident of our seedy dwelling was young medium-haired white cat who was so lame that she could only hobble obliquely across the floor. Her name was Guinevere, and I remember all of her injuries distinctly. She had suffered a farm accident with a moving combine, one of the occupational hazards of being a barn cat (life isn't all a comfy bed of straw, a saucer of milk warm from the cow, and all the mice you can catch). She had suffered a tibial and fibular fracture in her left rear leg, a broken pelvis, and complete destruction of the ligaments in her right stifle and hock (the knee and the ankle, in human terms). It was doubtful that the kitten could be made whole at any expense. Veterinary medicine is an economically awkward enterprise at best, dedicated doctors armed with modern medical techniques but animal owners that are often unable to afford care. This is particularly true on the small farm, where there is simply no room for expenses that don't offer some return on investment. The kitten had been brought to the vet school to be euthanized (an usually humane ending for a farm cat, suggesting that she had managed to form a bond with one of the family members, perhaps the farmer's teenage daughter). Veterinary medicine enjoys a peculiar brand of informal free-wheeling off-the-cuff charity when it comes to stray animals (or sometimes pets that become "strays" when an owner finds out how expensive it will be to fix their animal). When vets are faced with euthanizing an animal that could be saved, it is hard to simply "put the animal to sleep" permanently. It seems a life wasted.

When I heard that an injured "stray" had come into the school, I volunteered to take the kitten home and see if I could make it better. I had no idea what I was going to do for the cat, but I was leaving for my summer job at a veterinary clinic in a week and I hoped that my employer could help me.

The kitten's left tibia and fibula were fractured, fixable by taping the lower leg into a Thomas splint. A full-length outline of the leg was fashioned from aluminum rod; tape was applied to the foot and fastened to the bottom of the splint, producing an awkward appliance that was part crutch, part traction device.

The pelvis is a box-shaped structure that supports the hips and connects them to the spine; Guinevere's pelvis was broken in several places, but would heal (although a little crooked) with rest.

The ligaments in her right stifle and hock were beyond repair, at least with the techniques available in 1971. In a small kitten each ligament was almost as fine as a piece of heavy sewing thread, and the attachments to bone had been torn away completely. My boss helped me fashion support bandages to immobilize the joints; our best hope was that the tissues around the joints would heal enough to eventually support her weight. The kitten spent the summer at the veterinary clinic (thanks to the patronage of my employer), and the fractured tibia healed by September. The stifle was crooked but usable, while the hock joint healed with the foot pointing 30 degrees to the outer side. None of these injuries healed perfectly, but eventually we were content that the kitten could move around and wasn't in pain.

Every veterinarian has a collection of similar cases; whether we try to save a hopeless and indigent patient out of compassion and charity, or we are just too stubborn to give up on a patient when we know we could do something is a question, but those cases in which we don't have to spend a client's money or worry about liability offer opportunities to learn skills that are now learned more formally in internships or residency programs. Many of my most rewarding treatment successes over the years have been animals that I fixed for free and adopted out into loving homes.

This little white kitten also gave me my first experience with surgery. By the time I was ready to return to vet school in late August my employer suggested that I spay the kitten, since I was going to keep her.

I had watched Dr. Shelts perform the surgery a hundred times, but doing is different than watching. The fifteen minute surgery only took me an hour and a half, but I completed the first of tens of thousands of spay operations that I would eventually perform and my patient survived. I was now a surgeon. Sort of.

Guinevere returned to college and shared the Pullman apartment with Ken and I until the following summer, when a friend offered to take the now-full-grown cat to his parent's wheat farm, back to her humble beginnings as a barn cat. Soon enough I would start learning how to do surgery for real. But not for another year.

11

Gangster Microbes

The sign on C barn in the large animal hospital said "Quiet. And Stay Out!". I was taking a walk thru the large animal hospital on my first day back from Christmas break. "A" barn was well lit and the box stalls were filled with restless horses and a sheep that was half-shaved for surgery. A Herford bull chewed hay in a roomy pen in "B" barn, but C barn was dark and clearly off limits. Naturally, curiosity was raised: Did we have a quarantine for a viral epidemic? Hoof and Mouth Disease? Transmissible Gastroenteritis? I was trying to sneak a look thru the crack in the sliding barn door when Dr. Bracken walked up. "You need to see this case. You probably won't get to see another living case of tetanus while you are in school. But move slowly and don't make a sound. You'll see why."

Sliding the door open, I peered into the darkness. As soon as my eyes adjusted, I could see a large tan goat laying on its side on a bed of straw. Even in the darkness I could tell that the goat was recumbent, but tense. Dr B clapped his hands and the goat's body contracted so violently that he almost left the ground as he emitted a chilling cross between a scream and a groan. His neck was pulled back so forcefully that I was afraid that the goat would die before my eyes. I backed out of the barn quickly, followed by Dr. B.

"He contracted tetanus from a puncture wound when his leg was caught in a barbed wire fence. We are giving him tetanus antitoxin to neutralize the toxin, pennicillin for the bacteria that made the toxin, and a muscle relaxant to reduce the rigidity, but nothing is working very well. Any stimulation sends him into spasms, and there is nothing more we can do other than wait until his system clears the toxin. In the meantime, any noise can cause intense muscle contractions that could break his neck or stop his breathing." The goat was the easily most gruesome sight that I had seen so far, and the powerlessness of being unable to relieve the animal's suffering was disturbing.

The very word "disease" is associated in most people's minds with the infectious conditions caused by viruses, bacteria, and fungi. The mention of glomerulonephritis or pancreatitis barely raises a flicker of recognition in most people, but rabies, distemper, or anthrax are immediately understood and feared. Perhaps this is because many of the common infectious diseases have been controlled with vaccination and public health, making them mostly historic maladies that were vanquished by the medical heroes of the past century. When serious infectious disease does occur, however, it seems particularly malevolent.

I had taken Microbiology in pre-vet and learned about most of the common germs, but now I was introduced to the serious pathogens, the most-wanted criminals of the microscopic world. We grew the usual Staphylococcus, Streptococcus, and E. coli on culture plates, learning to identify each bug by the way it grew and changed the selective agar on the petri dish. Staph grew as opaque pearly white colonies, while Strep appeared as small pinpoints of clear matter, like droplets left on a window from a vigorous sneeze. E. coli, the most common intestinal bacteria and a frequent cause of urinary infection, grew in bright magenta colonies ringed with pink on MacConkey's agar. Samples from the culture plates would be placed on a microscope slide and stained with a dye containing hematoxylin (a blue dye) and eosin (a red dye). There were only two important features we used to classify bacteria microscopically: If the microbe stained blue ("gram positive") or pink (gram negative), and if they were round (coccI) or rod-shaped (baccili). E coli is a small gram negative rod, while Staph is a gram positive cocci that aggregates into grape-like clusters. Small pink-tinged colonies of Pseudomonas smelled like grape jelly, and when the petri dish grew a swarming carpet of greyish bacteria, the aroma of chocolate cake identified the organism as Proteus. (For some reason veterinary medicine is rich in food analogies: Roundworms are described as spaghetti-like, while tapeworms look like rice grains. The chunky pus of a Nocardia abscess is like cottage cheese, the bloody, mucous diarrhea of Hemorrhagic Gastroenteritis is described as raspberry jam stool, and the granular dark brown bits of semi-digested blood from a bleeding stomach ulcer are referred to as coffee grounds. The ear canal infected with the yeast Candida smells like rising bread. Every disease seemed to have a culinary reference.)

In Medical Bacteriology the focus was on microorganisms that caused various diseases, from Anthrax to Zoonosis. The bacterial diseases of large animals often had colorful names that added personality to the conditions: Lumpy Jaw, Blackleg, and Pizzle Rot (don't ask!). The infections diagnosed in dogs and cats sounded more scientific, but were just as feared: Leptospirosis, Bordetella, and Campylobacteriosis.

This parade of bacterial villains focused on the criminal element of the bacterial world, although we were starting to understand that most microorganisms are harmless, or even helpful. We learned that the internal environment of the body (Louis Pasteur's internal "terrain" where microorganisms live) determines whether a bacteria is harmless or causes a fatal infection. With a few exceptions, the trillions of germs in the world are not waiting to attack us and cause disease, but are simply living their own lives and minding their own business in their own selected environment. A microbe that is adapted to live in the soil and tolerate freezing temperatures during a harsh winter has no interest in growing in a living animal at 100 degrees with an active army of white blood cells trying to engulf it at any moment. So, why throw away a perfectly good donut just because it dropped on the floor and got a little dirt on it? Viewed from an ecological perspective, the microscopic world is a relatively peaceable kingdom. This was reassuring to me—there was a place for every organism, as long as you found your niche and took care of your business.

Even so, we were so focused on the germs of disease that we did not dwell on the importance of the multitude of harmless bacteria that we all carry with us; microbes were usually the villains in our medical stories.

There is one particularly malevolent family of bacteria that deserved its bad reputation. The various species of Clostridium shared characteristics that made them of medical interest. These are relatively large rod-shaped organisms, which stain blueish-purple with gram stain dye. Many of them include spores, small silvery seed-like objects within each cell. Members of this family are unable to grow in the presence of oxygen, like criminals that come out only after dark, but when they find their favored terrain deep within the tissues they become aggressively lethal. Several of the species have the ability to make nasty toxins. The tetanus bacterium, Clostridium tetani, produces the toxin that caused the spastic rigidity that I witnessed in the goat. In humans the name Lockjaw describes one of the symptoms that a person develops when they become ill after stepping on a rusty nail.

Even though the tetanus organism is common (and harmless) in horse manure, horses are particularly susceptible to tetanus if they suffer a wound deep enough to exclude oxygen. Giving an injection of tetanus antitoxin is the very first thing that a veterinarian is trained to do for any equine puncture wound. Dogs are relatively resistant to tetanus, but when it does happen the dog shows a somewhat comical appearance; the muscles of the head and ears become stiffly contracted, pulling the ears and eyebrows up into an exaggerated attitude of surprised attention while pulling the corners of the lips back into a "sardonic grin".

Two other members of the Clostridium gang cause fatal disease when they find their way into the muscles of cattle, and the diseases carry the suitably grisly names of Blackleg and Gas Gangrene.   And when the Clostridium perfringens bacteria living in a dog's intestine suddenly multiplies and produces toxins, the result is Hemorrhagic Gastroenteritis (HGE), causing "raspberry jam diarrhea" and profound dehydration.

The most famous member of the family is undoubtedly C. botulinus, which produces one of the most potent known toxins. We were told that if a coffee cup of pure botulinum toxin was dumped into the ocean and evenly distributed throughout the earth's water, there would be enough toxin in a glass of this seawater to kill a person; although I am skeptical of this claim, it is still a scary poison. The botulism bacteria, like all the members of its family, can't grow in the presence of oxygen, but it can grow in the sealed confines of an improperly processed can of vegetables. It also likes decomposing bodies, especially if they are submerged in the oxygen-poor water of a stagnant pond. Ducks and geese are affected when they sip water from a lake where an animal carcass has fallen, and the first signs are distinctively described in the name Limberneck. The head and long neck of the waterfowl hang down limply, and the birds often drown, even before the other signs of respiratory paralysis are seen.

The effects of botulism toxin have made it surprisingly popular for women who want to erase the laugh and frown lines of age.   Since the toxin paralyzes nerve cells, the tiniest amount injected under the skin of the face causes the muscles of expression go limp and the wrinkles go away. But, as the warnings state "there can be possible side effects with this treatment".

In our veterinary microbiology class we studied C. botulinum, growing it in broth culture tubes to protect it from oxygen in the air. When we used a glass pipette to transfer a few drops from the broth culture onto a microscope slide for examination the professor warned us sternly to use a rubber suction bulb to pull the broth up into the pipette, rather than sucking the solution into the pipette with our mouth. One student ignored the warning. Sucking a little too hard, he pulled some of the botulism broth into his mouth. Even though he spit it out immediately, he was already exposed to a lethal dose of toxin. An injection of botulism antitoxin can be life-saving, but the small community hospital in Pullman didn't have any of the serum. The toxin takes a few hours to paralyze the breathing and cause death, so a helicopter was summoned to rush him to a hospital in Spokane and save his life. Some of the most important lessons in medicine were not learned in lecture class; experience is often the best teacher, but the tuition can be high.

12

Doing Drugs

"What Are You Going To Do About It?" This hand-lettered sign was taped above my desk for many years to remind me that understanding is not enough. Up until this point we had been taught about the healthy animal and the sick patient. Soon we would be immersed in separating disease into convenient categories based on the type of patient (Jack Russell Terrier or German Shepherd Dog?), history (Did it start after the garbage can was ransacked, or has the onset been gradual?), signs and symptoms (Is the stool dark and tarry or gray and greasy?), and diagnostic tests (Are there large safety-pin-shaped bacteria in the stool under the microscope?) Although the satisfaction of making a diagnosis was gratifying, it didn't offer the patient any relief unless there was something that could be done to change the condition. Was there an "intervention" that might put the doctor between the patient and the disease? What are you going to do about it?

Physician and essayist Lewis Thomas observed that prior to the middle of the last century there were no medicines that were effective for any disease, and although that didn't keep doctors from prescribing pills and potions, people didn't really expect medicine to save their lives. The function of the physician wasn't as much to reverse the course of disease as to comfort the patient and let the family know what to expect: Was this cough just a cold that would go away? Was it pneumonia and survival was up to the strength of the patient? Or was it "consumption", the inexorable march of tuberculosis nodules through the lungs? At least the patient and their family could plan and worry accordingly. But not anymore. We have come to expect (sometimes unrealistically) that modern medicine can change the course of disease and restore health.

The very word "medicine" carries the dual meanings of the science of healing and the chemical compounds used to counteract the disease process. We have been armed with molecules that matter, invisible agents to tweak the basic machinery of life. In the middle of our second year it was time to "do drugs".

Pharmacology involved the details of antibiotics, immune supressives, hormones, sedatives, pain killers, and every other chemical intervention that might give us power over disease. We learned the effects of the drugs as well as their "mechanisms of action." It was not enough to know that penicillin killed some types of bacteria (or at least slowed down their growth so that cells of the immune system could clean them up)—we had to understand what the antibiotic was doing to the germs. Drugs in the penicillin family interfere with a specific enzyme that bacteria use to build a rigid cell wall, and taking away that support causes the bacteria to fall apart. We also had to know that some bacteria could produce their own enzyme, beta lactamase, which prevents penicillin from attacking the cell wall. Some bacteria lack a rigid cell wall, we learned, and therefore penicillin would be powerless to kill them. We also had to learn the potential side effects and the reasons that some patients might react poorly. How was the drug excreted from the body—through the liver, the kidneys, or by direct metabolism by the cells? Could the body view the drug as an invading substance, activating the immune system to create an allergic reaction, or even a severe "auto-immune" reaction?

The challenge of pharmacology was that we would be using molecules that we couldn't see to cause effects within the body that weren't visible. Our only evidence would be second-hand: We couldn't see the bacteria or the penicillin we sent into the tissues to fight them; we couldn't see the bacteria halting their growth or the white blood cells engulfing the bacteria to carry them away. All we could do is guess what was happening in the body from external changes: Did the fever decrease? Did the animal stop coughing and breathe more easily? And if these encouraging changes did occur, was it caused by the robins-egg-blue capsule? In a way we had to learn to be expert marksmen without actually being able to see if we were hitting the target.

Still, there is a feeling of power in learning to use drugs. A dose of cortisone would cause the white blood cells to stand down in their attack on the body, raise the blood sugar, cause an increase in urine, and give the animal a sense of euphoric well-being (or restless anxiety, depending on the dose). The animal's body was no long in charge when we used medication to control its functions.

It seems that modern medicine is criticized when, justly or unjustly, people complain that "my doctor just wants to give me a pill". It's true that drugs are a two-edged sword; often a pharmaceutical is the only thing that will reverse a disease process, but side effects and drug reactions are more common than we imagine when we reach for the bottle of purple tablets or the vial of an injectable drug the color of water. Skepticism is increased when new medications replace older ones every five years; what was the matter with the previous drug?

Even in 1973 there was a growing movement to look for "natural" solutions that didn't come with a "prescription required" label, and that movement has gotten stronger since, challenging the veterinary student and conscientious practitioner to consider all of the alternatives. The "natural philosophy" (sometimes described as "holistic") is partly a response to the realization that diet, lifestyle, and the animal's environment are often responsible for disrupting the balance of homeostasis and causing disease. The label of "alternative medicine" is misleading; every good physician understands that the terrain of underlying causes, including nutrition, stress, and genetics, combine to determine health or sickness.

Drug treatment for one common disease of cats underwent a series of changes as it was examined through the lenses of different specialties. Cystitis, or inflammation of the bladder, is common among cats. The signs are obvious: the cat sits in the litter box and strains to urinate frequently, sometimes with painful vocalizations. Eventually the cat distrusts the litter box and chooses to urinate on inappropriate objects, at which point the owner notices a bloody tinge to the urine and brings their kitty to the vet. In the 1960's cystitis was assumed to be caused by bacterial infection and antibiotics were prescribed (even though no bacteria could be cultured in 99% of the cases). In the 1970's viruses became the primary suspects, although we didn't have a drug for that. By 1980 nutritionists suspected that diet played a role, first the ash (mineral) level, then the magnesium content, followed by the moisture content, and finally the acidity of the diet. There was some decrease in the Feline Urologic Syndrome (FUS) as diets changed, but the condition continued to plague household cats. Finally a similarity was noted with a painful and recurrent human condition called Interstitial Cystitis, which was known to be a stress-related disease. Soon vets were using tranquilizers and anti-depressants to treat bladder disease.

Veterinarians can be mislead. In the case of FUS, attacks of bladder pain usually last for three days, even if untreated. It seemed like whatever treatment was prescribed was effective— after about three days. In most cases the problem reoccurred in weeks or months, and the doctor repeated the same treatment, because it worked last time. Now we accept that "Feline

Interstitial Cystitis" is primarily a lifestyle disease, and minimizing stress with "environmental enrichment" is the primary goal. The drugs that are dispensed for acute attacks are usually pain medications and anti-anxiety drugs. These drugs are usually effective—in about three days.

Pharmacology also taught us the power of placebo. When "sugar pills" work in human conditions we assume that it is because people expect medicine to make them feel better, the cultural explanation. However, placebos work in animals as well. When a new drug is tested for congestive heart failure in dogs, we know that a placebo results in an improvement in 30% of the patients. Thus, if giving the medication produces an improvement in 50% of the patients, we can assume that 30% responded just because we did something, and 20% were helped by the drug itself. Pharmacology was our opportunity to develop a critical perspective when deciding what drug to use and when. Even with a broadened view of the interventions available to treat animal disease, drug therapy remains the most powerful tool we have to modify disease, and we now felt like medical warriors, armed with an arsenal of pharmaceutical weapons at our disposal. Bring on the diseases!

13

A Clean Grassy Space

An old and wise adage states that "If the only tool you have is a hammer, every problem looks like a nail." If the only tool for healing was a pill, every problem would look like a metabolic imbalance, but some conditions are visibly structural in nature. There is no pill for a broken leg.

To the student the very essence of veterinary medicine was the art of surgery. It involved more than just using our brains to diagnose where the body had gone wrong, or what invasive microorganism or cancerous cell has hijacked the physical equipment of life. Surgery offers a direct way to fix what has gone wrong in a way that drugs cannot. "A chance to cut is a chance to cure". And of course, becoming a surgeon was romantic, bold, and even sexy. Before surgery the veterinary student is just an accumulator of knowledge. Then skill with a scalpel and hemostatic forceps places the power of healing in the hands in a literal sense. Every student looked forward to the second semester of the second year of veterinary school and a course entitled Introduction To Surgery. This was the coming-of-age for the future animal doctor.

Surgery has been an integral part of veterinary medicine for centuries. Stock doctors lanced abscesses and sewed up lacerations long before any effective medicines were available. (Farm vets had remedies, but they mostly seemed to consist of pumping large draughts of mineral oil and turpentine into a the stomach of a cow or horse, no matter what the ailment). The most common surgeries in large animals involved removing some part of the body to make the animal easier to handle: Horns and testicles were removed to make livestock more docile and less dangerous. Dog and cat surgery involved lots of removing of testicles and ovaries for population control as well, but in the 1970s more sophisticated operations were becoming more common. Even badly broken bones that previously caused a dog to be euthanized could be repaired with metal pins, screws, and plates. Paralyzing pressure on the spinal cord could be relieved by a dorsal laminectomy, removing part of the vertebra above the swollen spinal cord and scraping out the ruptured spinal disc. A blocked bile duct could be treated by creating a surgical bypass from the gall bladder directly into the upper small intestine. And in the ultimate act of life-saving heroics, a cancerous tumor of the spleen or intestine could be removed and discarded in the medical waste bucket. At that time, almost any surgery that was being done in humans could be attempted by a veterinarian, if the pet owner could afford it. Surgery was the arena where we would claim our status, not just as "animal doctors", but as physicians and surgeons.

Each student ordered our own pack of surgical instruments, and we handled our new hemostats, Olson-Hagar needles holders, and rat-toothed thumb forceps as if they were tools of magic. We couldn't wait to start learning the foundations of the surgical arts.

With eager anticipation we took our seats for the first lecture of Introduction to Surgery. On the blackboard were the numbers 1 thru 10, each with a blank space after it, waiting for the professor to fill each space with one of the sacred secrets of the scalpel. In our minds we were already stepping into a gleaming surgical suite and donning surgical gowns, gloves, and masks.

The professor's name was Dr. Keown, a name that we were not familiar with. Of course not—the realm of surgery was a world away from the everyday classes in physiology, nutrition, and endocrinology. The room was thick with anticipation; you could almost cut it with—well, a scalpel.

Dr. K was a plain man in his fifties, not the charismatic scalpel-slinger that we had imagined. After introducing himself, he walked to the blackboard and filled in the first step in preparing for surgery:

#1: Find a clean grassy space

There was a long moment of shock, disappointment, and lowered expectations among the small animal veterinary students. We were abruptly pulled down to earth from our visions of the shining hospital operating theater. It took a few minutes for the truth to soak in: Dr K was one of the large animal surgeons, rooted in the practical world of farm animal medicine, and farmyard surgery often required choosing a spot to operate that had the least manure. This class was intended to provide the foundation for all surgery, large and small, but Dr. K's perspective was based on his own decades of large animal experience

We would learn that large animal surgery was in many ways more difficult than the controlled operating room procedures of dog and cat medicine. First, the thousand pound patient had to be subdued, and while drugs were helpful, item number 3 on the blackboard was indispensable:

#3: Find two strong men to help.

Restraint of the patient could be a problem, and it often took more time to control a thrashing bull than to perform the procedure.

Everyone knows that surgery should be a sterile affair, and Dr. Keown's list gave it due. Of course, sterility could be somewhat negotiable with open-air surgery, and cleanliness was next to impossible. But a best effort needed to made.

#5: Provide a pail of water to soap and wash your arms up to the shoulder, and wash the surgical site as well as possible.

Sometimes the best that could be done was to make the surgical field two degrees cleaner than the environment and let the animal's immune system do the rest. Iodine was a favorite for disinfecting surgeon and patient, not because it killed all the bacteria, but because the reddish-orange color it gave the skin made it look sterile. Dr. K did give a nod to the importance of trying to achieve sterility in both large animal and small animal surgery; at that time even small animal veterinarians often performed spay and neuter operations without gloves or gowns. At least they washed their hands first, but even an old cow vet suggested we could do better and make it a rule to gown and glove after scrubbing in.

The riskiest part of a large animal operation comes after the surgery when it is time to let the animal come out of anesthesia and stand up on its own. Horses are so strong that they may break a leg by lurching to their feet before they are totally recovered, and a cow that has had a Caesarian section with a three foot incision in its abdomen can break open the muscle and skin of the belly wall by struggling to get up, resulting in the intestines dropping out onto the ground. The calf may live, only to become an orphan when the mother has to be sent to slaughter because of a dehiscence that spills a wheelbarrow worth of guts in the dirt.

#8: Keep the patient calm and lying down until completely recovered and help it up carefully.

After sewing up a barbed-wire laceration on a horse, number 9 was the most critical:

#9: Give every horse an injection of tetanus antitoxin.

The tetanus bacterium is common in horse manure, a harmless bystander unless it finds its way into the tissues where oxygen is lacking—such as a neatly sutured surgical incision. To have a horse with a routine wound develop the fatal spasms of tetanus a week after surgery was the worst of many disasters that could follow surgery

We thought that the last item on Dr. K's list was an attempt at humor. But we weren't sure.

#10: Present the bill and get payment while the patient is still alive.

This first lecture would be followed by many more, but several things were already clear. Things could go wrong in any number of ways and a feeling of foreboding accompanied the cutting and suturing more often than a sensation of heroic triumph. Thorough preparation was essential, but not sufficient to prevent the unexpected difficulty. And details make a difference, even when conditions are less than ideal. As we progressed through Junior Surgery class and the Senior Surgery Rotation, we hewed to these first ten principles. And before beginning a difficult and critical surgery (as when we joined the surgeons on one of the first total hip replacements for dogs with hip dysplasia), one of the attending students was sure to remind us: "Find a clean, grassy space".

Interlude 2

Hidden between the diseased tissues of pathology, the fearsome microbes of bacteriology, and the pharmacologic and surgical interventions to fight them was a different type of intervention. My relationship with Terri had progressed to the stage labelled "serious", and we spent every hour outside of class together. She was in her senior year, finishing up an Elementary Education degree to become the first in her family to finish college. During the fall/winter semester education students were placed as student teachers, working along side of experienced teachers as apprentice educators. Terri was assigned to a school in the southwestern Washington city of Pasco. The Tri-Cities of Richland (home of Hanford's atomic energy research and reactors), Pasco (home of poor migrant farm workers), and Kennewick (home of a thousand upscale houses left vacant when jobs at Hanford dried up and the physicists left), were nestled along the Columbia River just north of the Oregon/Washington border. Terri stayed with a family in Kennewick during her twelve weeks of student teaching, but each Friday night after my last class I would drive 120 miles to Kennewick to visit her, spending the weekend studying in her room before driving back to Pullman on Sunday night. Highways 260 and 395 cut southwesterly across the lower right corner of the state, and they were rarely travelled. My journey was a bleak drive straight across the sagebrush-lined two-lane, with only oncoming lights of the occasional semi-truck to break the monotony—the kind of drive that lulls a sleepy driver into running off the road. I avoided vehicular disaster, and the semester passed in a blur of sleep deprivation, poor nutrition, and lurid dreams of cirrhotic livers and cancerous growths. I hardly remembered attending the lectures and taking the tests, so I was surprised at the end of the semester that I had straight A's. Sometimes the best results come when circumstances are the most difficult.

Soon spring swept over the Palouse, and the chill wind hinted at change, Terri would graduate in June, but I still had two more years of fractious cows and mysterious dog diseases before I could leave Pullman. Our separation during Terri's student teaching semester convinced both of us that being apart wasn't an option and a decision needed to be made.

Looking back, I regret that I never properly proposed marriage. We both knew that we would be together, but I never had the nerve to make the grand gesture; there was no "will-you-marry-me" on one knee, or even a drive to the top of Kamiak Butte (the only thing that passed as a mountain in the Palouse) to offer her a ring. It happened in casual conversation: Terri mentioned that she would like to be married someday (but not until she graduated), and I replied that of course I wanted to be married, but I still had two and a half years of school to finish. Not a romantic way to decide to get married, but the decision came easily.

The hard part came when we considered the difficulties that came with the decision. The first question was how we could afford to finish my schooling. The modest support I received from my parents would end when we got married, and the current trend of taking out loans that were more than the cost of a house was not yet acceptable. The musicians that I had played with were graduating and drifting off from Pullman into the real world, and the gigs that had provided a little spending money dried up.

Terri started looking for a teaching job in the small towns of Whitman County, but schools were not interested in hiring a rookie teacher who would be leaving when her husband graduated veterinary school. She landed interviews at several schools: The

Catholic school in Garfield, twenty-five miles southwest of Pullman, the one-room school in Yellow Dog, and (most hopefully) the elementary school in Colfax. There was a lot of money in Colfax, since it was where wheat farmers moved when they sold their farms and became rich, and it was deeply conservative. Terri interviewed for a teaching position, during which she was informed that if she got the job she would be representing the morals and values of the town at all times. That meant that she could only be seen in public wearing a suitable dress; wearing pants in public would result in being fired. She was still stunned from this when the principal showed her the reading program used in the school. When Terri saw that they used the same Dick and Jane books that we remembered from our own first grades she blurted out "Are you still using those books?" The interview was over, and we had to consider other ways of supporting our new married life. It didn't change our mind about our decision; we had to follow the seemingly inescapable currents that had brought us to this place. We set a July date and trusted.

14

Strange Animals

Two years of sharing classes with fifty-nine other students should have fostered familiarity, if not comraderie, but socializing with my classmates was almost non-existent. I preferred my own company and time with Terri.

But I was a constant observer of the other humans in my class, with a combination of bewilderment and bemusement. Terri and I referred to the large animal students, most of whom grew up on ranches, as "Montana Cowboys", regardless of what state they called home. They wore big belt buckles, even bigger hats, and chewed tobacco, spitting into styrofoam cups that they carried with them everywhere. These were a foreign species, and keeping a cautious distance was not just a matter of cultural unfamiliarity. They suspected anybody who was not from a rural background of being a "degenerate hippie", probably stoned on drugs and brain-damaged from listening to heavy rock music. Back home in their small town, a male having hair that came down to his shirt collar or driving a nice car might be subject to a beating, but now that the cowboys were college students they could only talk about "taking care of those hippies" with their like-minded friends.

Pullman was a very long way from the Haight-Ashbury, and only one of our students could have passed even the minimum hippie requirements. Keith had long hair, a mustache, and was apparently a frequent user of psychotropic substances. Somewhere at the beginning of our second year he did "tune in, turn on, and drop out", as the slogan of the era suggested. Our class was then down to fifty-nine students, but everyone else continued through to graduation; the admissions committee did not want to waste taxpayer money on anyone who might not make the grade, and they had handpicked those applicants that they were certain would finish school.

Change was in the wind when I started vet school in 1970. Veterinary school had been exclusively male-dominated, and the number of previous female graduates could have been counted on one hand. The long history of veterinary medicine as a grueling job traveling from farm to farm treating large, powerful animals had made it a male profession. This was slow to change, even as sophisticated pet medicine was coming into its own. Our class of sixty included seven women, a record number. Particularly among the large animal students from Montana, Idaho, and Wyoming, the inclusion of women was greeted with disapproval and some derision. During large animal rounds one of the large animal students, (who had been a professional rodeo rider until he had broken so many bones that he decided to find a less dangerous occupation) muttered that he didn't know how a woman like Gail, a petite woman in jeans, boots, and hair straight down to her waist), would ever be able to control a horse taller than her head. The professor heard the comment and turned on him to remonstrate: "If you think that any of you guys are going to control a horse by being stronger than it, you are going to find yourself in a world of hurt. It is all in how you handle the animal, not in how strong you are". Gail didn't seem to take any offense. She was the most skilled horsewoman in our class, and by senior year even the ranch guys would come to her for help with a difficult horse.

Every class that followed ours had a greater proportion of women, and now veterinary medicine is a heavily female-dominated field, with more than 80% of the new small animal veterinarians (and a significant number of the large animal doctors) being female.

The top two academic students in our class were women, an early predictor of things to come. Shirley J (whose mild-mannered husband Gary was also in our class) was older and considerably more talented than the rest of us. The research professors would often give Shirley the data from their studies and she would write their papers for submission to scientific journals. Shirley had a kind but authoritative air, suggesting a benevolent young British queen. She went on to become dean of several veterinary schools in the US and Canada. Her friend Daphne H was from Hawaii; she was "that student" who everyone remembers from school: her hand was always raised to answer the teacher's questions, and she was devastated if she ever received a grade lower than an A+. Daphne and Shirley were lab partners, and the rest of us rarely entered their world.

That is, except for one good-looking student with an easy, flippant air of confidence and a way with everyone. I didn't know his background, but he had the aura of a privileged collegiate playboy. Dave G seemed to live a charmed life, and I was fascinated with the ease with which he handled the professors, our classmates, and everyone of the opposite sex. It seemed that he came to school from a different direction every day, depending on where the party or female companion from the previous evening had been located. He was also the only student that routinely missed any classes, but Shirley always took notes for him, keeping his grades high. One day Dave straggled in to Pathology Lab a half hour late and Dr. D berated him in his drill-sergeant voice, sarcastically asking why he had bothered to get out of bed and come at all. The dressing-down rolled right off Dave's back without effect. The following day Dave came into Pathology a half hour late again, but this time he was wearing his pajamas.

Dave's manner was so incomprehensible to me that I wasn't envious, just curious.

Reed R was only interested in reptiles, and found dogs, horses, and cattle uninteresting. Bob J came from his family's dairy farm in Spokane: he had a photographic memory and could quote page and verse from every one of our textbooks, but all he wanted to do was read about milk cows. Cicely C didn't seem to enjoy animals at all, and was only there for the science, our sole classmate who was headed for a research career.

It wasn't just that I had little in common with the other fifty-eight veterinary students; they each had their own worlds. To use autistic author Temple Grandin's phrase, observing my diverse classmates was "like being an anthropologist from Mars."

15

Terminal Procedures

Surgery teams started to form late in our second year and Mike, Leroy, Tim, and I continued to work together. The main difference was that now our dog would be a live animal. The first opportunity that we had to perform surgery on a living dog came in Physiology Lab, where we were to observe the effects of various drugs by surgically inserting devices into blood vessels and ureters to measure the effects of various drugs. We were looking forward to live surgery, but with deep ambivalence.

We would be putting a live animal through an unnecessary surgery for educational purposes, which went against our instincts. The dogs were anesthetized for the procedure, just as with any normal surgery, but at the end of the three hour exercise the dogs were to be euthanized without being allowed to wake up. Federal law required that any animal used in this sort of experimental surgery (termed a "terminal surgical procedure"), be euthanized at the end of the process. The law was very specific about how the animals were handled: humanely, but terminally. Considerable rationalization was needed to stomach this situation.

These dogs had been obtained from an overcrowded animal shelter, where they were deemed un-adoptable and would be euthanized the following day. After all, if they were going to be killed anyway, what was the harm of a few sleepy hours under a student surgeon's knife before receiving the final injection that would stop life permanently? It made logical sense, but it still felt like we were violating a guiding principle of reverence for life.

Our first experimental surgery in Physiology Lab taught another anatomic lesson. The goal of the three-hour procedure was to anesthetize the dog (it didn't feel right to give it a name), open the abdomen, and locate the left ureter, the slim transparent tube that takes urine collected in the kidney and transports it to the bladder to be stored for elimination. Once we found the ureter we were to slide a plastic catheter into it and connect it to an instrument that would measure the urine production as we administered various drugs into the IV to increase urine flow (diuretics) or decrease the output (anti-diuretic hormone).

Anesthesia and opening the abdomen went as planned, each of us taking turns using our surgical instruments to part the skin, separate the subcutaneous fat, and carefully locate and incise the linea alba (the fibrous white strip where the abdominal muscles from each side meet). After we created an eight inch opening in the abdomen, large enough to introduce a gloved hand, I reached in and searched for the left ureter. I couldn't find it where it was supposed to enter the bladder, but the ureter itself is only an eighth of an inch in diameter and transparent, so I knew it wouldn't be obvious. I withdrew my hand and asked Mike, and then Leroy, to see if they had any better luck. They were no more successful. Failing to find the ureter at its lower end, we took turns moving the intestines to one side to search for the left kidney, where the beginning of the ureter should be easy to find. Why couldn't we find it? Should we ask the physiology professor as he walked around the room to supervise? Did we want to look completely incompetent?—the kidney should be big enough to find easily!

As each of us took turns fishing around in the abdomen (which now seemed totally unfamiliar territory, like becoming lost in your own neighborhood) the clock moved on and our sense of frustration and desperation increased. Finally ten minutes from the scheduled end of the three-hour lab we gave in and called the professor over for help. He pulled on a pair of gloves and slipped his hand into the dog's belly. After fifteen seconds he pulled it out. "This dog doesn't have a left kidney. Sometimes that happens. Use the right one." We were too tired and discouraged to even share our looks of defeat and disbelief, so we slid a catheter in the right ureter, pushed the drugs into the IV, took our measurements, and sewed up the dog's abdomen . By this time it was an hour after all of the other students (and the professor) had gone home and the final moment of euthanasia became an exhausted anti-climax. There was an extended pause, an involuntary moment of silence, and then I pushed the plunger slowly. The pink solution of pentobarbital and dilantin used for euthanasia was brightly colored and more viscous than any normal IV drug, so that it was obvious that it wasn't a normal medication, to prevent it being given accidentally. I could feel the syringe vibrate slightly as the solution flowed through the needle; breathing ceased, the heart slowed and stopped, and it was over. I touched the cornea of the eye, the most sensitive spot on the body, and confirmed that there was no blink reflex . I had suddenly crossed over the line between learning about animals to being responsible, for better or for worse, for these fellow creatures.

It seems strange that ending life is so intertwined with saving lives in veterinary medicine, but "putting to sleep" pets in their final days is a routine part of the job. Dogs and cats have very few diseases that cause death suddenly, so the veterinarian is ultimately tasked with ending an animal's suffering when deteriorating quality of life makes euthanasia a humane necessity. Pet owners frequently comment, when they bring their dog or cat for that final visit, that they would wish it for themselves if they were near their own end. Perhaps they only say that to reduce the guilt which always goes along with euthanasia, and they might not actually opt for "physician-assisted suicide" when the time came.

Most of those people are sincere, and knowing that painful final days could be shortened is a comfort. In "right to die" states people who are able to obtain approval for euthanasia often live longer than other terminal patients that are unable to control the time of their own death. Human medicine struggles with this issue and its ethical, religious, and legal implications; veterinarians deal with it every day. You never get used to it.

It is easy, and perhaps unrealistic, to envy human physicians, who rarely are present at the moment of death for their patients. The cancer patient in hospice, the heart failure patient in the nursing home, and even the stroke patient in the hospital emergency room usually die one or two steps removed from the doctor who has cared for them for years. But nearly every day the veterinarian shares a small room with several crying family members as they ease their patient from life; in a way it is a privilege to share the final intimate moment, but the stress contributes to the "compassion fatigue" and high suicide rate among veterinarians.

As I pushed the syringe of solution into the IV, the realization still had not sunk in that I would have to perform euthanasia tens of thousands of times during my career. I made a vow that I would never put an animal to sleep if I didn't sincerely believe that it had no chance of recovery and was suffering. Occasionally this angered a client who felt that they should be the only one to decide if their pet lives or dies, but the commitment to using euthanasia only when necessary was the wall that made it possible to deal with death every day.

Even now I can feel the pressure of the syringe as I euthanized that first dog. Veterinary medicine became less romantic and more realistic.

16

Proud Flesh

The first time that I saw Jocko was during my freshman tour of the veterinary school, and I was both appalled and fascinated. In a box stall in B Barn stood a handsome horse, sleek, brown, and well-muscled. But as I looked down his well-formed legs I saw the monstrous growth around his right rear fetlock joint, just above the hoof. It looked like it could not possibly be a part of this beautiful animal. The swelling was the size of a basketball, encircling the entire leg. A few islands of haired skin were surrounded by an expanse of pebbly red tissue with occasional craters where blood oozed slowly. As menacing as it looked, this was not some life-threatening malignancy, but a uniquely equine problem known as "proud flesh". The horse's growth would be recorded in the medical record as "excessive granulation tissue", the result of the body trying too hard to heal itself.

Jocko's leg had become tangled in a loose strand of barbed wire and he suffered a deep cut just above his hoof. Unfortunately, the healing process was complicated. Producing new connective tissue is a necessary part of healing, but sometimes (especially on the equine lower leg) an explosion of immature cells multiplies and grows out of control. New blood vessels sprout into the poorly organized lump of tissue, feeding more expansion. Periodic bleeding within the granulation tissue results in calcified deposits, prompting even more layers of scar tissue.

Proud flesh is common in horses when a wound is not cleaned and the skin closed up promptly with sutures, but Jocko was an extreme case. He had been referred to the Large Animal Hospital in the hopes that the growth could be removed by our surgical specialists. The most daunting problem is that removal of the granulation tissue can stimulate the healing process even more, causing the mass to regrow with a vengeance.

Several unsuccessful surgery attempts were made during my freshman year, and every time I walked thru the barn I would stop by Jocko's stall to check on his progress. The leg was usually bandaged, but the bulky cotton wrap was always soaked with blood, suggesting that things were not going well.

Jocko was still living in B Barn during my sophomore year. By now his owners had given up on him, but the horse surgeons had not. This was really just a matter of too much scar tissue, and no equine surgeon could resist the challenge of curing a condition that could be handled with a scalpel. Jocko's owner had signed him over to the vet school to do with as they wanted, and a new equine surgeon had just joined the faculty who was willing to take over his care for free. Over the course of my second year several different surgical attempts were made, cautiously carving away layers of proud flesh and cauterizing the profuse bleeding with electrocautery, but now there was so much calcification that the mass, now fifteen inches in diameter, was too tough to yield to surgical instruments. Jocko languished in his stall, and I visited less often; the futility of his situation was too distressing.

At the beginning of my junior year, yet another new horse surgeon had arrived, and a team was assembled to fix the leg, once and for all. Jocko still showed hints of the beautiful animal that had arrived at the vet school two years earlier, but he looked worn, muscles diminished by disuse, and coat dull from lack of sunshine and grassy pastures.

On the day of surgery Jocko was led into the large equine surgery room, twenty feet by twenty, a high ceiling, and thick rubber matting on the floor and walls. Anesthesia solution flowed slowly into the horse's vein while a web of ropes gently lowered him to the padded floor as he lost consciousness. A hydraulic lift table embedded in the floor raised the sleeping horse to a convenient height for the ordeal that was to follow.

By the time Jocko was anesthetized and prepped for surgery I had joined the dozen students who had gathered around the edges of the room to witness the procedure with the morbid fascination of viewing the crash site of an eighteen wheeler.

Three equine surgeons surrounded the horse's leg, surveying the growth as if it was an angry Rottweiller. As soon as the scalpels were applied to the surface, there was blood everywhere. An electrosurgical "Hyfrecator" was used to coagulate the bleeding arteries and destroy tissues with an electric spark, but electricity and heat couldn't keep up with the hemorrhage as the surgeons struggled to see their surgical field. It didn't matter much, since the tissue was too hard to penetrate with sharp blades. Scalpels were exchanged for rongeurs, instruments that looked like large pliers with cups on the ends sharp enough to scoop away even bone. Conversation dwindled as the surgeons sweated and the smell of cauterized blood hung in the air.

After two hours and little progress, a surgical saw was employed; more blood, but only minimal progress. The observing students shared the sinking feeling that we would all experience someday when a critical surgery was not going well.

At the four hour mark the chief surgeon instructed one of the technicians to get a hatchet from the maintenance room and sterilize it. We all knew that if the leg could not be fixed the horse would be euthanized, and this was Jocko's last chance.

Once the hatchet was autoclaved the doctors took turns hacking away at the proud flesh, crunching thru the calcified tissue until they reached the normal bone below. The surgical drapes were covered in blood, the surgeons were covered in blood, the floor was covered in blood. At that moment the metal doors to the surgery room rolled open; a tour guide was showing a group of pre-vet students and their parents through the veterinary hospital. "And this room is where we perform all sorts of surgery on..." The door slid shut hastily.

Transfixed, we continued to watch patient and surgery, hope and despair, life and death. After another twenty minutes most of the excess granulation tissue had been removed and the bleeding had been controlled. There was no tissue covering the bone, but with some skin grafting the wound could eventually heal in. A multi-layered bandage was applied and it was time time to let the patient return to consciousness. The hydraulic table was lowered to the padded floor and spectators were ordered from the room so that Jocko could be kept quiet and calm. Anesthetic recovery is the riskiest part of any horse surgery, so every attempt is made to allow the patient to become completely conscious before encouraging it to stand.

Jocko's eyelids fluttered and he lifted his head a little. Then he lurched suddenly to his feet. A sickening crunch filled the room as the horse staggered and went down. The surgeons rushed to examine the leg upon which they had just spent four hours of skill and sweat. It appeared unscathed, and there was a moment of relief. But as the horse tried to struggle to his feet it was obvious that he had broken his front leg on the same side. Now there was no choice; after two years and the heroic attempts of the best horse surgeons, it was time to let Jocko go. The chief surgeon sent for a bottle of euthanasia solution, and as it dripped into the IV Jocko relaxed and lay down for the last time.

Junior year of veterinary school was underway.

17

All Creatures

Knowledge of the workings of the body and the many ways that things can go wrong was fascinating in its complexity and reassuring in its understandability. But in the third veterinary year knowledge met application, and it was clear that not every piece of information from lecture class could be matched to the living animal. And now the realms of "small animal" and "large animal" medicine took on different complexions.

They couldn't be more different. The aspiring veterinary student who dreams of treating complex cases in canine internal medicine and performing life-saving surgery on injured cats soon finds that they are faced with doors to three different worlds, and they have to enter all three: "Small animal medicine" dealt with dogs and cats and occasionally other small pets, while "farm animal medicine" taught the diseases and treatment of hoofed farm animals. "Equine medicine" had its own distinct collection of diseases and disabilities. There were similarities in physiology and anatomy among the animals, to be sure, but the medical needs of dogs and cats are closer to those of humans than they are to large hoofed animals. Even so, every student of veterinary medicine is required to become proficient in all species except humans (although one veterinarian I know served as a Green Beret in Southeast Asia, parachuting into remote areas to provide care for the elephants that worked the forest as well as the villagers themselves, and he found that he could treat both equally well).

The combination of pet doctors, food animal practitioners, and horse vets created a strange dynamic. Kids who grew up in the city and had been inspired by the family veterinarian who cared for their favorite kitty were suddenly expected to learn about farm life and know how to use a halter and a squeeze chute. Every patient in the barn seemed like a large and dangerous being from another world. It wasn't much better for the student who grew up on a ranch in Montana or a dairy farm in Spokane; they knew about cows and most of them had been raised with dogs, but farm dogs were a rough lot and were rarely cared for beyond their useful years. Strangely most of the ranch kids who had no qualms about pushing around a thousand-pound bull but were scared to death of cats. But we all had to learn the ways of these different worlds.

Even the economics of large and small animal medicine were completely different. As a small animal student, I took it for granted that my job would require me to use all of my resources to return the sick pet to health. Only later would I learn that this goal would always be subject to the ability of the dog or cat owner to pay for treatment. Equine medicine was similar in some ways, but pleasure horses didn't get as much attention as performance horses, where the goal was to improve the horse's ability to run and jump competitively, preferably in time for the next race. In what was termed "food animal medicine", every decision was measured in profit and loss. This meant that the large animal doctor had to do what was best for the herd and the bottom line; the fate of the individual cow rested on whether diagnosis and treatment made business sense, and if not the cow was likely to be sent to slaughter.

In small rural towns the "mixed animal practitioner" is still in demand, vaccinating and spaying dogs and cats in between farm calls. The lines of specialization are less rigid, but any serious case is likely to be referred to a veterinarian in the nearest large town with the expertise and equipment required. As veterinary medicine has become more sophisticated there are too many new medicines and techniques for every doctor to know it all and after graduation most of us would have to focus on just a few species.

In a way, learning the different skills needed to treat all animal is like learning to become an auto mechanic to fix family cars (dogs and cats), and discovering that you also had to become competent in maximizing the performance of Formula One race cars (competition horses) and long-haul semi-trailer trucks (food animals) in which the death of a patient was less of a problem than a cost overrun. On top of that, you discover that the different vehicles run on different fuels, have different combustion systems, and are supported by different types of suspensions. Finally, you discover that some of the vehicles are prone to exploding (race cars, horses) or crushing you to death when they go out of control (semi trucks and cattle). Oh, and one last thing: you have to do all of your mechanic work without turning off the engine, and parts are unavailable.

Thus, every student was tasked with learning not only the different worlds of pets, horses, and food animals, but also the entirely unrelated art of surgery. Surgery didn't really have much to do with medicine, and presented an entirely different set of perspectives and skills to learn, whether the patient was a show dog getting a hip replacement or a cow that needed a caesarian section to deliver her calf.

By the time I entered veterinary school I was focused on small animal medicine. When I was much younger the allure of horses made me picture myself treating beautiful Quarter Horses and temperamental Arabians, but my family sold our horses when I was in eighth grade and my enthusiasm faded. I also realized the dangers of working with horses; when I was twelve years old, I was kicked in the groin when I approached one of our horses from behind. The colt was only six months old, but the lesson was not lost on me and I was thankful that he was only as tall as my chest. Although the younger me had harbored a fantasy of owning a cattle ranch, it eventually dawned on me that my medical care would be lavished on cows whose fate would take them to the meat counter at the grocery store. An interest in dogs, cats, and other pets was more than sufficient to motivate my studies, even if that meant acquiring knowledge about large animals that I would surely never use.

The core daily lectures of third year were divided into Small Animal and Large Animal, and veterinary medicine started to seem more real as the details of specific diseases were described. They were complicated, but straightforward. An explanation of the pathogenesis of the condition might be followed by a list of ten signs to memorize, a description of the tests that would be done to confirm the diagnosis, and a clear-cut plan to treat the disease. There was less thinking and more rote memorization than I expected, but I started to gain confidence that I could eventually diagnose the fungal pneumonia of Coccidiomycosis (a regional disease also called Valley Fever) when I would be called upon to diagnose a dog that was coughing, losing weight, and had recently moved from Arizona. I knew that I could diagnose Mitral Insufficiency of the heart when I heard the characteristic lup-fwish of a left-sided heart murmur and the x-ray showed an enlarged heart pushing upwards against the trachea. Even the complicated hormonal diseases like Cushing's Disease, in which the adrenal gland churns out excessive cortisone, seemed to follow a recipe of signs/blood tests/treatment. If I had any premonition that in real life the borders between different conditions were vague, the symptoms would be misleading, and the treatments less than effective, I don't remember it. This was supposed to be what being a real doctor was like. The pile of hand-written lecture notes on my table started to build up until they were taller than my head, and my task was clear: Memorize everything that I had written down. It would all make sense when

I finally had a real coughing dog in front of me. I finally felt a sense of what it might be like to practice medicine, but that would change.

Interlude 3

Autumn of junior year quickly turned chilly, with an early October storm blowing down across the Palouse from the Okanogan region on the Canadian border. Small dry snowflakes stung my face but left only a shallow bitter crust on the plowed fields where winter wheat had been planted.

It was warm enough inside the two cramped rooms of our Married Student Housing unit on South Fairway. Terri and I had been married in July, despite the financial uncertainty that the next two years would bring. The ceremony itself was simple, a dozen guests at Terri's childhood church on a day that threatened rain, until the weather relented and turned sunny. Terri looked beautiful in a thirty-dollar empire-waist wedding dress from a bargain rack, the plain wedding bands were borrowed from Terri's parents (who were no longer using them), and I wore a sunshine-yellow tux and a ruffled shirt. The vibe was completely early 1970's.

Our first year of married life was full of storybook poor-but-happy romanticism. The only job that Terri could find was at the student union cafeteria, making sandwiches and cleaning up after the tobacco-spitting cowboys that spent their leisure hours "shooting the bull" at the lunchroom tables. I taught a few guitar lessons to supplement our income, but together we could only scrape together a hundred dollars a month.

We found a place to live in South Fairway, a cluster of units that had been constructed as temporary housing for GIs during WWII and apparently never updated. The outsides of the duplex apartments were painted "government brown" and the insides consisted of a bedroom and combination kitchen/living room with an oil heater in the middle which provided a barely adequate source of heat. But rent was fifty dollars a month and we were happy to find a place to live.

Rice was cheap, and we discovered that the local supermarket butcher gave away dog bones from their butcher shop for free. There were enough scraps of meat clinging to the bones to provide rice-and-dog-bone-casseroles for the entire week. When she could, Terri would smuggle me one of the poor-boy sandwiches that she made at the cafeteria.

None of these starving student privations were unbearable. There was always the expectation of a financially secure life after graduation, and we kept a written "someday list" of future promises to bolster our optimism. The weather was cold, but times were good. Graduation was two years away, but junior year seemed like a turning point, a hill from which we could see our future in the distance. And even though South Fairway had a no-pets policy, we shared our home with several animals.

Casey Cat didn't seem to mind the cold when she went out on her daily explorations. She had a luxuriant medium-length coat of black with a white chest and paws and a knack for finding hidden spots to warm herself. She was the first addition to our new family.

One of the occupational hazards of working with animals is that the veterinarian, even as a student, becomes a repository for all manner of unwanted, incurable, or inconvenient animals.

Terri's younger sister had adopted a cat the previous summer, and when she left for college a few months later she thrust the cat upon us. Casey had the good manners not to sun herself in either of our two windows where a passing university maintenance truck might spot her. And despite the bitter weather she loved being outdoors, so we could always claim that she was a roving stray if she was seen. Casey had the ideal area to roam; just behind our unit was the university golf course, with rolling grassy fairways lined by bushy overgrown roughs and a shallow drainage ditch. Golfers were only on the course when weather permitted, which meant September and May, so she had the fields to herself. Casey Cat would usually be gone until early evening, but we could never discover what she did during the days. Her domain would have been a great hunting preserve, but we never saw any evidence that she had caught any mice or birds. Some cats leave their comfortable first home to visit some second home where a cat lover might feed them or pet them, but Casey didn't seem to seek human companionship and she was always hungry when she came to the door at night for us to let her in to eat and groom herself by the oil heater. Except for the most inclement weather Casey would follow her routine at all times of the year. Even when the weather was a bitter 10 degrees, she would return when she was good and ready, and her fur wouldn't be cold to the touch. Casey shared the ability of most cats to find the warm sheltered spot when needed, and she never complained.

What Casey did complain about was riding in the car. She hated the car, the cat carrier, the driving, everything, and she would meow loudly and anxiously until the car stopped. Mostly we avoided taking her in the car, but on holidays we always drove to Bellevue and Kirkland to spend time with our families, and that meant six hours of constant feline vocalization. The third time that we had to take her on our drive, she was nowhere to be found on the morning of the trip. We searched and called for an hour, but finally had to explain the situation to a sympathetic neighbor, who fed her and let her into our place at night. A few months later we once more had to leave, but this time we were determined that we would give Casey no clue of our plans. We wouldn't get the cat carrier out of the closet, we wouldn't pack our suitcases, we wouldn't turn down the oil heater, and we wouldn't even talk about our driving plans if she was in the room (you never know!). But once more, when we were ready to leave she was gone. We searched, but again we had to ask the neighbors to let her in and feed her. When we returned from this trip we thanked the neighbors for watching out for her again. But then they told us that Casey was right back there on our doorstep as soon as our car drove away. We could not figure out how she knew that we were leaving or how she knew that we had gone and it was safe to come out of hiding, but now we had a plan. The next time we needed to leave and she disappeared we drove away in the car, but turned and drove back around the loop that ran around South Fairway. As predicted, there was Casey, sitting on our doorstep. When we got out, she greeted us in her usual manner, we picked her up, put her in her carrier, and listened to her complaints all the way across the state. As perceptive as she was about our leaving, she never learned this trick of ours, and every time we left and drove back around our road she would be waiting on the doorstep.

In her second year with us Casey disappeared on one of her daily jaunts and we never saw her again. As all cat lovers do, we feared the worse but told ourselves that she had just made other arrangements. All of her roaming seemed to be confined to the golf course, so being injured by a car seemed very unlikely. There were probably coyotes and stray dogs, and perhaps even a bobcat, but she seemed so canny, so able to take care of herself, that we doubted that any of these would be her match. We knew that the apathetic animal control officers in Pullman would never bother to chase down a wary cat, but we visited the shelter just to make sure. We told ourselves that she had probably befriended someone who wouldn't force her to ride in an automobile, and decided to move in with them.

Not long after Casey's disappearance we took in a homeless puppy, an adorable mix of German Shepherd and Husky, eight weeks old, brown and fuzzy with a mask of black over her muzzle. We knew that keeping a large dog out of sight from the housing managers would be more difficult than hiding a cat, but the puppy needed a home.

I named her Naima, after a ballad that jazz saxophone legend John Coltrane wrote for his first wife. I had worn out my vinyl record of Coltrane playing the composition at the Village Vanguard, and I told Terri that I thought it would be a great name if we ever had a daughter. When we named our new puppy my wife encouraged me to use the name, likely as a defensive move to keep me from using it for any possible future offspring we might have.

We tried our best to keep Naima out of sight as we raised her through her puppy stages of house-training, learning to walk on a leash, and barking and whining when we left for school and work, but after six months the maintenance truck came by when we walked out of the house with Naima on a leash, and within a few days we received a stern letter from Student Housing telling us to get rid of the dog or move out.

There was no other place to live that we could afford, so we did what pet owners often do when in a tough spot: we begged my parents to take Naima, at least for the rest of the school year. My dad and mom had tolerated my animal-keeping during my growing-up years, and they reluctantly agreed. They had a spacious, nicely landscaped back yard at their house in Kirkland, and figured that she wouldn't be much of a bother.

But one of the characteristics of Huskies and other northern breeds is that they like to dig and chew. Digging may be an adaptation to burrowing into snowbanks to keep warm at night, and chewing may result from the high energy of a dog bred for hard work and easily bored. But I had not yet had an opportunity to see these breed tendencies up close. Naima had chewed up her share of household items during her first few months, but we accepted these as puppy mischief, and we didn't have many household items for her to destroy.

My parents graciously took Naima when we returned to Kirkland for spring break, and she seemed to like her new home. When we came home for summer break a few months later, however, we found out what devastation a ten-month old puppy can accomplish. All of the plants in the yard that were small enough for her to reach, including the rhododendrons and my mom's favorite seven-foot-tall cypress tree that she had planted months before, were chewed down to the ground, with only frayed stumps where the stems and trunks had been. Then Naima had turned her energies into digging holes. The grass areas of the yard looked like a battlefield pocked with foxholes. Naima had dug out of the fence repeatedly, despite all of the usual remedies of burying chicken wire two feet down into the dirt beneath the fence and placing immovable rocks along the inner side of the fence. Naima was so proficient at excavation that she would dig a hole under the fence, and after a short burst of freedom she would dig a different hole to get back into the yard. My parents sympathized with our predicament, but we had no choice other than to find Naima a new home. This was a pointed introduction to the challenges of veterinary medicine: There are human circumstances attached to every patient.

18

Cut to Cure

Surgery seemed like magic; learning to take an animal apart and sew it back together was the high point of veterinary school so far. During third year our apprenticeship began: Junior Surgery.

Surgery and medicine are art and science, yin and yang, action and deliberation. It is likely that early surgery, dating back 4500 years (in Egypt) to 5300 years (in India) was of greater benefit than any medical treatments of the ancients. In antiquity more lives were saved by surgery than by medicine, even though hemorrhage and infection took their share. And the results of surgery could be seen, unlike effects of draughts and potions, which could only be imagined. In the 16th century Ambroise Pare summarized the direct, intuitive appeal of surgery: "To eliminate that which is superfluous, restore that which has been dislocated, separate that which has been united, join that which has been divided, and repair the defects of nature." We wanted to do that.

Learning surgery was literally a hands-on study. The very word "surgery" derives from the Greek for "hand-work". But the learning curve was steep.

Every Friday each team of four students practiced surgery on living dogs. Again we were ambivalent about sacrificing a real animal for our education, but at that time there was no alternative (there are now some "dog surgery simulators" to spare the real dogs). The animals that served as surgery subjects were already on death row at the animal shelter, but we still felt guilty about our role. The same dog was used each week, but he didn't seem to mind. In fact, he thrived on the attention that he received. On the non-surgery days we would visit our dog in the ward to see how he was doing, and we were always greeted with enthusiastic affection, face licking, and let-me-out-to-play exuberance. Most of the surgery dogs had lived difficult lives as strays and were underweight and ragged looking, but over the months of Junior Surgery their weights and spirits improved and their initial distrust of humans quickly melted away once they had food and attention.

Our dog looked like the classic stray: medium sized, with medium-length hair and a medium length muzzle. He was the classic "ancestral-type dog", similar to the companions of human hunter-gatherers before humans started selecting for short faces, long hair, skinny legs, and tiny or giant body sizes. If all our our purebred dogs were turned loose in the wild to interbreed freely without human interference, this is what dogs would look like in only a few generations. Even in our modern dogs this native conformation brings with it "hybrid vigor", increased physical health and a more stable personality. The dogs kept by Native Americans and nomadic people across the world tend toward this type, and even today many of the farm dogs (what I refer to as "real dogs") share this appearance. Our dog was a real dog, and we named him John.

Our surgery team included myself, Mike, Leroy, and Tim, and our first procedure was to neuter John. There was nothing tricky about the operation, other than that my hands felt like I was wearing mittens. Neutering doesn't require opening a body cavity or cutting thru any tissue other than the skin to expose the shiny tunic covering the testicles. It was my turn to start the procedure and with a flick of my scalpel the tunic opened and the testicle popped out. The most important part of the operation involved the spermatic cord and blood vessels that provide circulation to the gonads, and these had to be securely tied off with suture to prevent bleeding. A Kelly Forcep with two-inch curved and grooved surfaces was clamped across the vessels, a knot of braided suture was placed securely around the cord and vessels, and Mayo Dissecting Scissors were used to separate the testicle from its connection. As soon as the cord was cut it was obvious whether the clamp had been placed properly; on my first attempt the testicular artery spurted blood high enough to leave tracks on my surgery mask and double my heart rate. After repositioning the forceps to stop the hemorrhage I placed another strand of suture material just below my clamp and tightened it down as snugly as I could so that it wouldn't slide off and cause a disaster of post-op bleeding. Then all that was left was for Mike to sew the edges of skin together, using a continuous pattern of stitches to bring the edges together from underneath so that there were no protruding knots that the dog might chew on. John recovered from anesthesia with no difficulty, and greeted me with the usual enthusiasm when I came by to check on him the next morning. I would go on to repeat this surgery many thousands of times in my career; spaying and neutering are not glamorous, but a necessary part of everyday practice for the small animal veterinarian.

Not only did our surgery dogs accept their weekly operation happily, but they seemed to relish the routine. Friday was surgery day, and most of the dogs seemed more excited than usual when we greeted them Friday morning. After the first few weeks we could let the dogs out of their kennels, open the ward doors, and they would run down to the prep room, ready to be anesthetized and clipped up for surgery. They seemed to welcome any form of human attention.

Most of our surgeries involved removing some tissue that we might eventually have to take out to treat some tumor or infection. We removed testicles and ovaries, a kidney, a small section of the liver; it surprised me how many parts and organs the animal can live without. We opened the stomach (which would come in handy in the future when we had to retrieve a ball or a pair of underwear that the dog ingested) and resected the intestine, cutting and reattaching sections of the intestine like plumbers (a personal experience, since I had two similar surgeries when I was a small child).

In our fifth week we opened the abdomen and removed our dog's spleen. Although the spleen serves a function in storing extra blood, providing immune cells, and assisting the bone marrow in making blood cells, it can be removed with no adverse effects. This is fortunate, since both benign and cancerous tumors commonly occur in the spleen. It even seems to play a part in the most dreaded surgical disease, gastric torsion, in which the stomach fills with air and twists, cutting off circulation to other organs and rapidly leading to death. Dogs may be better off without the spleen. After opening the abdomen the spleen is easy to find, since it floats free of the other organs except for the eight or ten large vessels that shuttle blood to and from the organ. Every one of these vessels had to be cut and securely ligated; failure of one surgical knot could cause fatal bleeding into the belly. We were really careful. If one tie was good, then we would use two or three on each vessel for good measure.

We moved on to more challenging surgeries. Although we understood the basics of each surgery, we certainly were not trained in the meticulously gradual way that human surgery interns are. There was no chance to assist an experienced surgeon perform the operation, holding clamps and putting in the last few sutures. We were just told what surgery to do today and if we ran into trouble we could send one of our team out the the prep room where the surgeon was relaxing as we sweated out the procedures. At first this caused alarm and anxiety, but after the first half-dozen surgeries it just caused anxiety. The surgeries became progresssively more difficult as we learned to create a bypass between the gall bladder and intestine (for a blocked bile duct), remove a kidney (for a tumor or stubborn infection), and repair a torn diaphragm (diaphragmatic hernias are usually a result of the animal being hit by a car, holding its breath at the moment of impact, and tearing the broad fan of muscle that separates the chest and abdomen and moves to inflate the lungs).

Repairing a diaphragmatic hernia is simple enough, but it is one the most stressful and dangerous surgeries that we were allowed to perform. The idea is simple: open the abdomen, pull the liver back to visualize the diaphragm, locate the tear (which we had to create, since John's diaphragm was normal), and sew it up. But the surgery is fraught with difficulties, even for more experienced surgeons. The first problem is that the diaphragm provides the vacuum seal that pulls air into the lungs when the ribs expand on inspiration. If the diaphragm has a hole in it, then air rushes from the abdomen into the chest through the opening and collapses the lungs. This places the responsibility of expanding the lungs on the person who breathes for the patient, pushing air in and out of the lungs through a tracheal tube. We didn't have a respiratory machine, just Tim's hands on the black rubber bag, putting just enough pressure on the bag to fill the lungs with each breathe without causing excessive pressure that might rupture the lung's tiny alveoli. Tim held John's life in his hands, but Mike and I had to find the diaphragm, which is hidden by the stomach and liver and can't be reached easily.

Depending on where the diaphragmatic tear is located, a partial glimpse may be all that you can get. The surgeon has to reach in with a curved needle on the end of long needle holders, working in a hole to catch each edge of the muscle and tie a series of knots to pull the edges of the torn muscle together. A number of other important structures must be avoided as they course through the diaphragm: The aorta (biggest artery in the body), vena cava (the thin-walled largest vein on the body) and the esophagus (which is weak and heals poorly) all cross the diaphragm and threaten danger for the surgeon. Puncturing any of them with the suture needle results in immediate disaster. In a real-life diaphragmatic hernia there is the added problem that a lobe of the liver, or most of the stomach, may have protruded thru the diaphragmatic hernia and be trapped in the chest, crowding the lungs. Even if these organs can be pulled back into the abdomen where they belong they may release stagnant blood that has been trapped in the organs, and the rush of this deteriorating blood can crash the circulation. Our diaphragmatic hernia surgery was performed on the seventh week of the semester, after we had performed a half dozen other routine procedures. But what happened wasn't our fault.

Since repairing a torn diaphragm required a tracheal tube and an oxygen/anesthesia-delivery machine, we could not use the injectable anesthesia methods used for our other surgeries. The vet school had only enough anesthesia machines for half of the surgery groups, so some teams used the machines and performed diaphragm surgery while the other half performed a different procedure, removing one of the adrenal glands. Our group did the adrenal surgery first, followed by the diaphragmatic hernia the following week. Dogs, as well as the rest of us mammals, have two adrenals, one on each side, nestled next to the kidneys. The adrenals produce a variety of substances to help us cope with stress (adrenaline and cortisol), as well as hormones that control fluid balance. Dogs can do just fine with only one adrenal, since the opposing gland grows larger over a period of time to provide the needed stress hormones. Removing the right adrenal was a simple procedure, although the proximity of dangerously large blood vessels like the vena cava made it feel like diffusing a bomb. We wished our hands were more steady. At least we had our own full complement of stress hormones to sharpen our focus and pump up our circulation. Our dog recovered with no noticeable effects.

The following Friday arrived and we took our dog back to surgery to practice a diaphragmatic hernia repair. This surgery was more difficult; as Mike retracted the liver and stomach away from the diaphragm I reached deep into the recesses of the abdomen and made a modest size tear in the thin muscle. Instantly I could see the lungs, looking pink and bubbly. Without the diaphragm the lungs collapsed and stopped inflating when the ribs moved, so Tim started inflating the lungs with the rubber bag on the anesthesia machine. Immediately I could see the lungs inflating against my diaphragmatic "hernia" and receding as the pressure on the bag was released. Sewing up the hole that I had made in the diaphragm took some time, since I couldn't visualize the diaphragm while my hands and forceps crowded the incision. Eventually I had to feel my way, using touch to guide the suture needle to the edges of the muscle. The hole in the diaphragm was closed and Leroy stepped in to close the abdomen. The surgery went as well as it possibly could, but our dog just wouldn't wake up from anesthesia. His blood pressure and heart rate dropped lower and lower, even as we pushed more fluids through the IV. A rising feeling of foreboding took over as we watched helplessly. Why wouldn't our patient respond? We called in the surgery professor, but he had no answers as we watched our dog, which we had grown fond of, gradually fade away. After thirty minutes of resuscitation attempts, it was over. Our first surgical loss. As we turned away from our dog and looked around the room, we saw that a number of other surgery groups were also watching as their patients died on the table. The previous week all of the hernia surgeries recovered without difficulty, but this week all but two of the seven dogs did not wake up from surgery. Post-mortems were performed, but there was no evidence of bleeding or organ damage. The next day the surgery teacher apologized; he should have known, he admitted, that the dogs with only one adrenal gland would not have been able to produce the cortisol and adrenaline needed to withstand a stressful operation. It was slim consolation, but we learned a lesson. Once in practice, I always pre-medicated any diaphragmatic hernia surgery with a large dose of intravenous cortisone to supplement the stress-busting ability of the patient's own adrenals. This was a hard lesson in considering the entire patient, as well as learning to anticipate any of the variety of disasters that can occur when we enter the body in our effort to do good.

Since this experience was nearly at the end of the surgery semester we did not have to sacrifice another dog to our surgical inexperience. We skipped the last two procedures ("you'll figure them out when you have to"), and instead we spent Friday afternoons doing spays and neuters for the animal shelter.

Federal law required any experimental animal to be humanely euthanized after it had competed its purpose. The laws were written to prevent callus misuse of laboratory animals, but it broke our hearts to be asked to euthanize these otherwise healthy animals just because they had finished their usefulness. Mysteriously all of the surviving surgery dogs disappeared from the kennel, one by one, at the end of the semester. Rumor has it that each surgery group found a way to let their dog escape to a home outside the vet school, and if one of these dogs should be noticed walking around campus with a student, the surgery teacher would deny that he knew anything about it.

Junior surgery included large animals as well, but patient volunteers were in short supply and the procedures were minor and done under the guise of necessary procedures. The only horse surgery that I remember was a "standing flank approach" to the abdomen, in which an incision was made in the flank of a horse that was sedated but standing and conscious, using local anesthesia as one member of our team held firmly onto the halter. When I made a four-inch incision in the muscular side of the horse (intended to allow a sterile gloved into the abdomen), I severed an artery that crossed the line of incision. The artery spurted pulses of blood in a graceful arc over my head. I ran to Dr Bergevin, a horse practitioner who was spending a few months at the school helping with the students, and asked what we should do about the spouting of blood. He glanced over at the horse and calmly told us "Nothing. It's a long way from the heart". Apparently horses have a very ample supply of blood, and a pint or two is hardly worth mentioning.

There were other surgeries to learn in cattle and sheep, as well as horses, but we skipped them; we could learn those during our clinical rotations senior year. We already had enough blood on our hands.

19

Fowl Deeds and Foul Plants

Knowledge can seemingly give one the ability to walk on water—even though the water may be only a half inch deep. Education should confer a depth of expertise, but there is also something to be said for broad and shallow. Veterinary medicine covers so many sciences and species that my studies barely touched some subjects. I avoided many of the elective classes, such as Therapeutic Horseshoeing and Dairy Herd Management, but there were some esoteric subjects that were required of all students, regardless of their level of disinterest.

The most universally disliked of these was Avian Pathology. Professor Kenzie, known by all as "Chicken Sam", was devoid of any semblance of personality. He was a short, dumpy man with a bristling ring of spiky gray hair around an irregular bald patch. He was always seen in a stained lab coat that reached to his knees as he shuffled around the laboratory wing of the vet school.

None of the sixty students in our class had the slightest interest in birds, and this was our sole introduction to the feathered patients that we might chance to see someday. The only diseases that we studied were those of commercial importance to poultry farmers, which meant that treating individual birds was never considered. "Flock health" meant sacrificing any bird that looked ill and performing a post-mortem to see if was affected by a contagious disease.

The first thing we learned is that all sick chickens look alike; droopy, listless, and emaciated. With no external clues to aid diagnosis, that meant that any sick chicken was quickly killed to prevent the spread of disease through the flock (which would later bring to mind the Monty Python scene in which plague victims were piled on the dead wagon protesting "But I'm not dead yet"— supply your own Middle Ages accent). The diseases were unfamiliar to us: Merak's Disease, Newcastle's Disease, Fowl Cholera, each with their own signature necropsy findings. One problem with the study of Avian Pathology was that outbreaks of the diseases in question were rare (at least in Eastern Washington) and we never saw an actual case. Since real cases were not available to study, we had to create our own. Young chicks were infected with the various pathogens, and the birds rapidly sickened with the diseases. In the lab we were told to sacrifice the infected birds and slice them open to observe their livers, kidneys, and airsacs. This was one of the most objectionable tasks in our veterinary education. Some of the students from farm backgrounds weren't squeamish about wringing the necks of their infected chicks, but most of us could not bring ourselves to kill with our bare hands. The alternative was only slightly less gruesome: an electrical cord was provided with a plug and two clips. One clip was fastened to the chick's beak, the other to the cloaca (anus), and the plug was inserted into an electrical socket, instantaneously electrocuting the fuzzy yellow chick and nauseating the student executioner. Although this process was to be repeated every week in lab, after the first session most of us found someone who had the already killed their subject and looked over their shoulder. We took a quick look at the internal lesions and wrote up a quick description in our lab log. Chicken Sam would stay for the first ten minutes of each two-hour lab period and then retire to his office. Perhaps he already knew that none of us cared about seeing the ravages of Fowl Cholera and that the lab would be empty ten minutes after he left. None of my classmates ever worked in a job in which skills gained in Avian Pathology were useful, and even though I would eventually take care of pet birds in my practice, chicken electrocution never provided me any useful knowledge.

Poisonous Plant class, on the other hand, while it was equally useless to future small animal doctors, was an interesting and entertaining hour on Thursday afternoons.   Plants that are harmful were certainly relevant to those who would treat hoofed grazing animals, since horses, cows, and sheep are likely to eat anything that grows and suffer the consequences.   Dogs and cats occasionally ingest plants that have ill effects, but those are usually ornamental landscape plants like lilies or azaleas, and these were not part of the course.   Poisonous plants usually taste bad (plants would rather not be eaten at all rather than kill their consumers hours later), and intelligent carnivores have better things to get into, such as the spoiled contents of an overturned garbage can.

Poisonous Plants had a macabre fascination; when a cow eats water hemlock it convulses violently, frothy bubbles will come out its nose, and it collapses into a morbid mountain of beef that can't even find its way to a dinner table. The horse that eats loco weed will become addicted and search out the bad-tasting plant, which eats away the brain like crack cocaine until the horse dies in a twitchy delirium.   The effects of plant poisons made infectious diseases and even cancer look benign by comparison.

But the professor who taught the class made bad botanicals come to life.   Dr Farrell was a robust and jolly character who would pace back and forth as he told stories of the dangerous plants lurking in pastures, woods, and swamps. He told us about Death Camus, a low flowering plant with a tuberous bulb. Native Americans in southern Washington gathered the common Camus as a staple in their diet, but the bulbs of the aptly named Death Camus were fatal. The only time the two varieties of Camus could be distinguished is when they were flowering in the spring, not when the bulbs were harvested in the fall. Dr E would act out a scene of the Native American gathering tubers and trying to remember "was this the patch that bloomed purple last spring, or were they white?". Then he would tell us the scientific latin name for the plant, Zygadenus, drawing out the name like a horse race announcer: "Aaand it's Zyyyyygaaadenus rounding the far turn and into the homestretch!". It was easy to remember even the obscure scientific name for an obscure bulbous plant.

Every dangerous plant on Dr. F's Most Unwanted List seemed to have its own way to kill. Oleander, the flowering ornamental shrub used along California's freeways, triggered fatal heart attacks in the unlucky horse that finds one of the leaves in his hay. Lupine (both the high lupine found high in the mountains and the low lupine found low in elevation) was teratogenic, causing monstrous birth deformities in sheep that graze the flower early in the season, when snow still covers the other vegetation. Bracken fern contains thiaminase, an enzyme that destroyed the essential B vitamin thiamine, causing severe vitamin deficiency and paralysis in horses. (We were also warned to refer to the plant as Bracket Fern when we worked under the chief of bovine medicine, Dr. Bracken.) From my Colorado childhood I was already familiar with Astralagus, the "loco weed" that causes addictive dementia; as children we were warned to never let our horses graze those weedy patches in the nearby meadow. A different sort of brain damage occurs in horses that consume the yelllow-flowering Tansy plant, common in Eastern Washington. This plant causes liver failure and a buildup of toxic ammonia in the brain, resulting in a zombie-like state in which a horse spaces out and walks aimlessly for miles, heedless of gullies and barbed-wire fences. This disease earned the picturesque name of Walla Walla Walking Disease.

We also learned about the plant toxins that found medicinal uses. Sweet Clover Disease occured in the spring when lush growths of clover in moist pastures spoiled and became rich in dicoumerol, an anti-coagulant so potent that cattle start coughing up blood and died. Pest control companies marketed dicoumerol as the rodent-killer D-Con. Naturally, pharmacologists realized that this would be just the thing to give people who were at risk of blood clots and strokes, and now it is prescribed as Warfarin.

My wife had a fondness for beautiful blue periwinkle flowers, and she seemed to resent it when I repeatedly explained to her that the perennials that she loved produced vincristine, a substance so toxic to the bone marrow that it was used in micro-doses as a chemotherapy drug.

Tiny doses of digitalis from the Fox Glove flower have been used for centuries to strengthen the contractions of a failing heart—or larger doses could be used to poison an unpopular monarch, if that is the direction you wanted to go.

And the Pacific Yew tree had a potent toxin in its bark that provided one of Dr F's favorite one-liners: The Latin name for the Yew is Taxus, and he would remind us that "Nothing in life is sure except death and Taxus". In smaller doses, however, Yew bark finds use as a chemotherapy for breast cancer.

Dr F turned Toxic Plants class into a favorite diversion from the intensive large and small animal medicine classes, but the professor had other esoteric interests in which the vet school indulged him. He studied a diarrhea-causing microorganism carried by a parasitic fluke that infested wild carnivores, and it was he who kept a full grown bear caged in the large animal barn to study Elokomin Fluke Fever and Salmon Disease. A caged wild bear with chronic diarrhea, who can resist that? He was also interested in the effects of freezing tissue, which led him to invent freeze-branding, a method of putting a ranch's identification on the hide of a cow painlessly and permanently by freezing the brand into the skin.

In fact, Dr F would try freezing anything. When one of the small animal dermatologists was faced with an incurable case of demodectic mange (a disease caused by a microscopic eight-legged mite that lives in the hair follicles), Dr F suggested that they freeze the skin to kill off the mites. After anesthetizing the dog he sprayed the entire skin with liquid nitrogen until it froze as solid as the layer of ice on a lake in winter. The dog's body temperature plunged down into the 40s, creating a "what have we done?" moment, but he was able to revive the patient, raise its body temperature, and bring it out of anesthesia. After a few days the dog's skin started to slough all the outer layers, like a combination of sunburn and freezer burn. As the skin continued to peel off, he again wondered "what have I done?", but rationalized his extreme approach by insisting that if the dog couldn't be cured it would be put to sleep anyway. After four weeks in the veterinary hospital, the surface of the skin healed and hair started to grow. Eventually a luxurious haircoat grew in where the mange had been. His risk had paid off, but even Dr F wouldn't repeat the experiment.

Education doesn't always involve practical information. Seemingly useless knowledge may suggest an unexpected connection that is relevant in an unrelated area. Or sometimes useless trivia is simply interesting to know. Jeopardy host Alex Trabek claimed that he loved learning about things in which he had no interest. Curiosity for its own sake can be an antidote for too much useful learning.

Interlude 4

After five years of college, fatigue was starting to settle in. With the exception of our experimental surgery subjects there had been no chance to care for a real animal patient, and ultimately our only surgery patients sacrificed their lives for our learning process. Being married provided solace and support, but there was never a carefree honeymoon period to relax and adjust to meeting each other's needs. Our families were six hundred miles away and preoccupied with the struggles of our younger siblings; we never heard from either of our families. Our life felt very alone.

The Palouse winter added to the feeling of desolation. The snow wasn't deep, but only because the bitter winds blew it off the furrowed hills.

By late March it seemed like winter had gone on forever and the tedium of my schooling and Terri's menial job were no relief. The small amount of money that we had saved from our summer jobs was nearly gone. We needed an escape, even if it was only temporary.

One Sunday the temperature soared into the upper 40's, and even though snow still covered the ground Terri and I decided to drive our rusting Ford Falcon to the Moscow Mountains in Idaho for a picnic. Strangely, no one else was out on the backroads that led to the park, and the park gate was locked. We parked on the snow-covered gravel shoulder and walked around the gate until we found a picnic table and scraped the snow off. We shivered a little as we ate our lunch, but the chilly air and the impending end of my junior year gave a strange feeling of freedom. Maybe it was the hope of the future in the air.

After we enjoyed all of the cold freedom we could stand, we packed up and returned to our car. Slipping it into gear, I found that the tires were stuck in the snow and loose gravel of the road's shoulder. We pushed, we put straw from along the road under the tires, we tried rocking the car back and forth to push the wheels back on the pavement, but nothing worked. A sense of alarm gradually grew as we realized that we were stranded miles from any human habitation in the unforgiving end of winter and we had seen no vehicles pass on the road since we had stopped.

At first, we just sat in the car. But soon we could feel the chill as the afternoon sun dropped lower. This is the moment in most stories when help miraculously arrives from nowhere, and suddenly we heard the sound of a vehicle approaching from a distance. Soon a worn pickup truck appeared and I waved my arms to draw attention. The truck slowed, but then resumed speed as it went past. Our broken hopes recovered when the truck pulled over a hundred yards down the road and crept in reverse toward us. Asking help from strangers had always been hard for me, but necessity overcame that difficulty.

The driver of the pickup rolled down his window, and the first thing I saw was the rifle on the gun rack behind him. Then he spoke: "What do you think you are doing out here?"— and not in a friendly, helpful tone. Sometimes stereotypes ring true, and this Idaho farmer fit the typecast, in oily overalls and rubber farm boots. His tone warned us that we were not out of trouble yet as we explained our predicament.

The Palouse Country was, and still is, aggressively conservative, and in the early 70's the tension between the isolated rural inhabitants and anyone perceived as a liberal hippie-type was intense. This farmer had likely seen anti-war protestors rioting on TV and pictured an epidemic of pot smoking, acid tripping college students. It didn't help that I had a beard, hair that touched my shirt collar, and drove a rusting junker of a car. We must have been those hippies he had been hearing about.

I explained that we had just come out to the country for a picnic, but he looked unconvinced. I thought I saw him glance back at the rifle on his gun rack. Eventually he seemed to come to the conclusion that it was better to help us and be rid of us than to leave us there, so he backed up his truck and pushed us from the snowy shoulder onto the road. His truck then sped off before I could thank him. We drove back to Pullman in silence with the feeling that perhaps our hopes were premature.

Life doesn't always take note of what we are or are not ready for. Later this same month our lives took another turn; Terri announced that she was pregnant.

A feeling of excitement struggled with a feeling of apprehension about how we might have a baby and survive my last year of school. In the face of uncertainty, we felt the need to celebrate, as if false confidence would help it all work out. It had been years since we had eaten at a restaurant, but I made reservations at the Hilltop, Pullman's only nice eating spot. We had only enough money for this one last splurge, but we needed something to show ourselves that we had faith in this future that had been thrust upon us.

In 1972, pregnancy was still considered incompatible with working any sort of job, and as soon as it was apparent that Terri was expecting she was relieved of her employment in the student food services. No other job would even consider hiring a pregnant woman at that time, so we had to look for ways to obtain some sort of income. While we enjoyed our celebration dinner at the Hilltop it occurred to me that a swanky place like that might need live music, and I approached them about playing solo guitar during dinner hours. They agreed to try me for a week for $100, enough to get us thru a month of my final vet school year. After a week of late night gigs the restaurant decided not to make music a regular thing, which was fortunate; playing music until 11PM after ten hours of school and two hours of studying each evening was proving to be impossible.

The only skill I possessed that didn't involve a regular job was music, so I took on a few guitar students and also taught a beginning adult guitar class for the city of Pullman's activity center, enough to play several months more rent.

Terri's father had been a homesteader in Alaska in his younger days, and still had a permit to "harvest" a moose, and this year he shot his last moose and gave us the meat for our winter provisions. We were able to stretch the meat for most of the year. Strangely, despite our circumstances we did not feel like we were poor, not in the way that an unemployed worker in a big city or a rural family struggling to put food on their table was. Even though the light at the end of our tunnel was a year away, we knew that it was a temporary condition, one that would end the following June.

20

Meet Your Meat and Care for Your Health

Learning for its own sake is part of a well-rounded education, and the remainder of third year was spent rounding out our knowledge with things that I hoped I would never use.

Large Animal Medicine was a required class, even for those of use who had seen enough of both ends of hoofed animals to last us. The most entertaining part of large animal medicine was the names of the diseases, which were doubtlessly being used by farmers in the 19th century and before. Veterinarians used science to explain these ailments, but the common names didn't change. Cows still suffered from Wooden Tongue and Lumpy Jaw, and these names persisted even after the infections were identified as Nocardiosis and Actinomyceticosis. When a nail or piece of wire was swallowed and worked its way thru the wall of the second stomach of a steer, it was useless to refer to it as a Reticuloperitonitis; farmers only knew it as Hardware Disease (which is not the same as the human condition in which a husband is allowed to browse Home Depot unattended). Foot Rot affected sheep, calves developed Scours, and horses died of Colic. Even the future small animal veterinarian needed to memorize every detail of these picturesque ailments as we we imagined fanciful cartoon versions of the diseases.

Those of us who were headed for small animal practice hoped that we would never use any of the information or see one of the mud-and-manure-spattered animals, but still had to learn enough to pass the tests and the state board exams before graduation. Every decade or so veterinary colleges and state boards decide that it is a waste of time and resources to teach dairy cow vets the details of every canine and feline condition, and to teach urban small animal practitioners how to diagnose a cow with Shipping Fever, but there has been limited movement to allow species-specific licensing. Every vet is expected to know everything. Perhaps this is because the profession still has one foot in rural America, where the doctor is expected to treat the calf with scours and dispense medication for the dog's mange, all during the same visit. As we rounded out our education, we wistfully thought of human medical students, who had only one species to deal with (although humans have their own peculiarities, to be sure).

To further round the education, the spring semester featured lecture classes in Public Health (who isn't for public health, after all?) and Meats.

That's right, Meats. Every morsel of hamburger, steak, or pork chop that is sold in America is looked over by a licensed veterinarian, and each student needed to know the rules and regulations that would qualify us to be USDA Meat Inspectors (an ironic salute to the USDA would be appropriate here). We had to learn how to spot a sick cow as it dragged itself into the slaughterhouse, and we had to be able to check every carcass for pathology. Some conditions, such as Cancer Eye (common in white-face Herfords that spent their days out in the sun) caused only the affected parts to be discarded, while other diseases, such as pneumonia or a liver abscess, required condemnation of the entire carcass. The packing plant didn't like it, but the meat inspector's word was law. There were lots of people in the industry (including starving veterinary students) who would have taken their chances with a steak from cow with "just a little" pneumonia, but security was tight in the meat packing plant; condemned carcasses were locked away in a secure vault until they could be properly disposed of in a hygienic manner. The penalties for violating these rules were stiff enough to keep anyone from considering purloining the beef.

Part of our education as meat inspectors involved a field trip to Spokane to visit three different slaughterhouses. As junior students we should have been immune to the blood-and-guts aspect of meat production, but the scale upon which cattle and pigs were processed was disturbing. The meat processing plants were located in industrial areas or on the outskirts of town, since the facilities were surrounded by strong odors. Inside the buildings the smell was even more oppressive, and air we breathed seemed to be filled with a fog of microscopic fat droplets. We were assured that the animals were killed in a humane manner, but in order to drain the blood from a carcass the heart had to continue beating for a while. Cows were rendered unconscious with a "knocking gun", an air-driven bolt that delivered a blow between the eyes, while pigs were anesthetized with carbon dioxide before being suspended so that the blood could drain out by gravity. Many of us started to question our meat-eating ways. Even more alarming were the areas where scraps of meat and fat were collected from every surface (including the floor) for making bologna and sausage; there is truth in the saying that it is far better not to see how sausage is made; once something is seen, it can't be un-seen.

Our all-day slaughterhouse tour came with lunch. At a steak and burger place nearby, where we could still smell the factory odors. I chose a salad.

As medical professionals, the subject of Public Health seemed like a reasonable topic to study. After all, many animal diseases can also infect people; for instance, salmonella is impossible to eliminate from poultry-producing farms (as is campylobacter, which is more common but less notorious), and a variety of parasites, from certain stages of canine roundworms and hookworms to one-celled toxoplasma and giardia protozoa, can affect humans. It would be good to understand the diseases, termed zoonotic, that can be shared with animals. We learned that veterinarians are trained as public health officers, and can find employment in government agencies whose job it is to protect the well-being of the human population. Military veterinarians have told me that one of their chief duties was latrine inspection.

None of the veterinary students in our class were inspired by this professor to go into the public health sector. Our lecturer was a long-haired hippie-appearing man in his 30s, who appeared to own one set of clothes, faded jeans and a wrinkled shirt. He lived in a teepee in the Moscow Mountains and his family had some sort of diarrhea all winter long from their primitive living conditions.

Dr. P had a philosophical approach to epidemic diseases: History has taught us, he said, that when a new bacteria or virus first starts to cause illness in an animal or human it is often devastatingly pathogenic, killing most of its victims. From the microorganism's viewpoint, however, this is not advantageous. Why kill off the animal that is providing you a nice place to live and reproduce? Over time, these organisms (and their hosts) adapt and the disease becomes less severe, allowing the host to live (miserably, perhaps) and spread the organism among its friends and relatives. For example, he explained, archeological evidence tells us that measles was a uniformly fatal disease several millennia ago, and now it has evolved to a tolerable childhood infection. Unless you develop one of the serious complications, that is. He proposed (apparently seriously, despite being employed to teach us how to prevent these illnesses) that we really shouldn't try to fight these diseases, because they will become less serious over the next couple of thousand years.

What about the plague?, a student asked. Interesting story, he told us. The plague bacteria, Yersinia Pestis, is still with us, and is carried by many wild rodents, such as chipmunks and ground squirrels. During the Middle Ages, it favored the House Rat, and spread to humans by way of the rodent's fleas. As its name suggests, the House Rat not only invaded human dwellings to steal food, but it also made its home in our nooks and crannies. At night the rat's fleas would hop off and bite the human inhabitants, giving them a touch of the Black Death. Efforts were made to eliminate the rats (although it wasn't clear if people understood that rats carried the disease—theories like malignant vapors from nearby swamps were more in vogue). What finally stopped the epidemics of Plague that decimated Europe was a new kind of rat. The Norwegian Rat moved in across Europe and displaced the House Rat as the resident rodent. Norway Rats carried the plague bacillus and invaded human dwellings looking for food, just as their relatives did, but they made their nests and slept outside, sparing the humans the plague-carrying flea bites. See, all things work out on their own in time, our teacher reassured us. We all made a reminder in our notebooks: avoid handling any sort of wild rodents.

One assignment brought Meats class and Public Health together. Each student was required to visit a local supermarket and purchase a pound of hamburger, and take it to the bacteriology lab for culture. Nearly every sample contained one or more potentially pathogenic bacteria, most commonly E coli, the most common "coliform" (fecal) bacteria. Don't worry, the professor reassured us, cooking kills all those bacteria. Just don't touch raw meat with your hands. The Public Health class, like the Meats class, was required, but everyone was given a B, no matter how uninterested (or nauseated) they were. It was all part of the rounded education, and as junior year came to an end we promptly forgot the unnecessary information and got ready for senior year— real medicine, real patients, real responsibility.

21

Shadows

From the top of Kamiak Butte we could see all the way to Idaho, and halfway to Spokane. The Butte was the highest point in the Palouse, although modest by geologic standards. Its summit rose a thousand feet above the wrinkled and folded wheat fields below, a refuge for pine trees and tall grasses.

My final year of veterinary school started the following day and the August temperature was uncomfortably hot, so Terri and I to drove up the hill for cooler temperatures and a last picnic before the start of classes and clinical rotations.

Senior year was different from the previous three years; no longer could I just sit in lecture classes, studying my handwritten notes every evening to absorb the lists of symptoms and treatments in solitary. There was no way to avoid interaction once Clinics began, and although I looked forward to visiting with the patients I was nervous about dealing with the clinicians (some of whom had fearsome reputations) and communicating with pet owners. These final nine months would be the most interesting and memorable.

Fourth year students still attended four hours of lecture each morning, but the early mornings and all afternoons were devoted to Clinics, during which we would treat hospitalized patients at the direction of the staff veterinarians. This was our apprenticeship, where day-to-day routine drudgery met the struggle of restraining an unwilling patient or puzzling through a diagnostic challenge, and making an honest mistake could cost a patient's life or cause legal entanglements. It seemed that real-life cases never fit neatly into the lists of symptoms that we had memorized and the lines between learning and application, science and skill, became blurred.

Each week brought a new clinical rotation, shared by three or four other senior students working under the direction of an experienced veterinarian One week would be spent in Radiology, and the next might be Small Animal Surgery, followed by Bovine Medicine or Clinical Pathology. Each of the supervising doctors had some idiosyncrasy that students from the previous rotation warned about, but I would usually try to complete my duties without being noticed, hoping that the doctor would not walk up and start asking questions to which I had no answers. Suddenly everything—every answer and every unskilled movement of the hands—mattered.

My first week of clinical rotations started in Radiology. Taking x-rays of coughing dogs and limping horses seemed simple enough. CAT scans, diagnostic ultrasound, and MRI machines were still in the future, so our most advanced imaging involved pointing a beam of x-rays at a suspect body part and capturing the rays that were able to penetrate the tissue onto an 11x14 piece of film coated with a silver-containing gel which bonded to the film when activated by the radiation. Since light would expose the film in same way as the x-rays did, the developing process had to take place in a darkroom, where the student would open the latches on the film cassette in the dark, feel around for the sheet of film, and clip it onto a wire frame before dipping it for two minutes in a developing tank (the acrid smell of the solution I found strangely pleasant), one minute in a water rinse, and then into a fixative solution for five minutes to rinse away the areas of coating that had not been activated by the radiation. Finally the film was hung up to dry. Radiology had its own charm, the anticipation of magical answers as the developed sheet of film was held up to the bank of light boxes in the Radiology office. Had the dog's leg been broken in the accident? Lift the film to the box and the answer appeared, perfectly clear: the bone was intact, just some swelling in the surrounding muscle. The patient would likely be back to normal after a week of soreness. Occasionally it even happened in that way, but because most of the patients in the University Veterinary Teaching Hospital were referrals of difficult cases from veterinarians around the state, most of the easy answers had already been taken.

The more typical case was the hazy spot on a lung, the possible enlargement near the adrenal gland, or the jagged bulge of the bone over the mid-shaft humerus (which could be a bone infection, an early tumor, or a traumatic hemorrhage under the fibrous bone-covering periosteum). Each picture was a collage of light and shadow, and even the chief radiologist admitted that his interpretation was guesswork at best. The key to reading radiographs was said to be having a good "imaginator".

We learned that deciphering x-ray pictures depended a lot on the patient. Dogs in particular come in all shapes and sizes, and no matter how the x-ray parameters were set (time, miliamps, and kilovolts, to be specific), the radiation passes more easily thru a five pound Chihuahua and gives more detail than an x-ray beam focused on the far side of a hundred pound Rottweiller. Horses present a mass so bulky that radiographs of the chest or abdomen look like a picture that one might imagine in the clouds above. As it happens, everything that goes wrong with horses involves the lower parts of the leg, the lameness problem. Taking x-ray images of horse hooves and fetlocks turned out to be the simplest procedure to learn. Even though the radiology department had several state-of-the-art x-ray machines, students were sent out to the barn with a small portable unit that looked like a rotary-dial phone, an ancient hand-held x-ray generator attached by three feet of cable to a black Bakelite control box with one large knob. The labels for the settings had long ago been worn off, but it didn't take much imagination to know that they had once been marked "1", "2", and "3". Even in our first week of veterinary clinics the three small animal students in my group were able to figure out how to take a picture of a limping horse: One student held up a cassette containing a sheet of x-ray film to the side of the horse's leg, a second student selected the setting where "2" should have been, and the third student held the handpiece of the x-ray generator up the opposite side of the sore leg and ordered the person on the controls to fire the button. After developing the film in the darkroom the pictures looked good to us; we could tell there was a bone there, and some other white and grey stuff. We were now radiologists.

The dangerous reality of veterinary medicine appeared on the second day of radiology rotation. A large Rottweiller with bulging muscles and and a very bad attitude was admitted to take radiographs of its hips. One of the most common crippling conditions in large dogs is hip dysplasia, in which the hip sockets are too shallow, causing instability and severe arthritis at an early age. Since fifty percent of the cause of hip dysplasia is hereditary, breeders of large dogs usually have x-rays taken of the hips before deciding to breed. This particular Rottweiller was probably an aggressive dog on its best days, but the anxiety of being in a strange room with unfamiliar smells and mysterious mechanical whirring sounds turned him into a snarling storm of thrashing and snapping; he would need to be anesthetized to take the pictures, the chief radiologist explained, holding a 20cc syringe of sodium pentothal in his hand. My job was to restrain the dog, positioning myself behind his shoulders with his head in the crook of my left elbow and his right front leg circled by my right thumb and fingers. The first thing the panicked dog did was to throw his head straight back and up toward my head, snapping with lethal intent. Fortunately I had lowered my head to his neck as I struggled to restrain him, so rather than being bitten in the face, my cheek took a hard blow from the top of his head. There was no way to let go of the dog safely, so I held on long enough for the radiologist to seat the needle and push the plunger to inject the initial dose of anesthetic into his vein. I will relive the next moment forever; the angry dog collapsed limply to the floor, but not in the gradual tapering of consciousness typical of anesthesia. His heart had stopped, and he died instantly. Every effort was made to bring the dog back to life: Heart massage and injections of stimulant were ineffective, and in minutes it was all over; we had killed the first canine patient that I touched.

Later the radiologist lamented that he should have known not to inject anesthesia into a dog in that state of aggressive panic, with adrenaline blasting through his bloodstream. Anesthesia and adrenaline are a dangerous mixture, a lesson that I carried with me every day in practice. I wasn't present when the doctor gave the client the bad news; the dog they hoped would be a star breeding stud had passed away from an anesthetic "reaction". The realization that veterinary medicine would be a minefield of potential disasters started to soak in.

Ever since the time of Hippocrates, physicians have been guided by the principle of "primum non nocere": First, do no harm. Doctors in every age have taken an oath to avoid any medical action that might leave their patient worse off. In reality, avoiding harm is not possible. Any treatment that has beneficial effects can have side effects. It is up to the doctor to weigh harm and benefit, but professional education largely focuses on the benefit side of the scale,

Even though I was only a participant acting at the direction of the doctor who administered the fatal anesthetic, I felt the knife edge of responsibility keenly. I replayed the episode in my mind for weeks, repeatedly experiencing the tightening in my chest that I had felt as the dog went limp in my arms. I had known immediately when it happened that the dog had died; I could almost feel the dog's soul slipping thru my fingers. Forty years later I still feel apprehension every time I give an anesthetic drug.

Taking responsibility for a patient no longer seemed to be a contractual relationship; instead, it became a visceral connection, a bond formed of worry and anxiety, every effort shot thru with a small dose of dread of the unexpected. But the more miserable a patient was, the easier it was to put aside the apprehension and get to the task at hand, motivated by the good we sought to do. In the end, each sick patient needed us.

22

Feline Misery

My first feline patient looked as miserable as a cat could possibly look. His eyes and nose were crusted with yellow discharge and he made snorking noises as he struggled to inhale through his nose. Cats hate to open their mouths to breathe and will continue to attempt nasal breathing unless it is absolutely out of the question. This cat was emaciated and sat with the hunched posture of a severely ill cat. The disease was already familiar from infectious disease lectures: Feline Rhinotracheitis is a severe respiratory ailment caused by a herpes virus, extremely contagious and full of misery.

The second week of clinics brought two other students and myself to the isolation wards, where deadly pathogens ruled. The Feline Infectious Disease Ward included a dozen cages, every one of them holding a depressed, sneezing, drooling patient. Treatment for the disease was intensive; it took an hour, three times daily, to administer antibiotics and subcutaneous fluids to all of the cats, clean and lubricate their eyes and noses, and coax them to eat (usually without success). Cats are very dependent on their sense of smell for their appetite and if they can't smell they won't eat. Clogged nostrils make it impossible to chew food and breathe at the same time, even if the cat is willing to try. We attempted to clean the nasal passages with saline solution, but our efforts were unsuccessful and unappreciated. To make things worse, painful ulcers often spread across the tongue, making the cats resistant to any attempt to examine the mouth.

Cats that were sick with "Rhino" often had fevers that ran up to 105 degrees; fever is part of the immune system's strategy of fighting infection, forcing the animal with an infection in the wild to lay low and not waste energy searching for food. But fever is not helpful when it persists more than a few days, causing dehydration and muscle wasting.

There were ten cats to care for on our morning treatments. I chose Rommel, a black cat with a white bib, for my first patient, perhaps because he reminded me of our Casey Cat. He had once been a commanding animal, master of his neighborhood, but now he looked like a person who had been stranded in a lifeboat for a month while suffering from the flu. His nose was crusted with mucus and so raw that he would not let me touch it. I lifted a fold of skin over his shoulders, and instead of sliding neatly back into place when I released it the skin stayed tented up, indicating that Rommel was at least 10% dehydrated. I checked the clipboard that held his medical record and noted that this was his third week in the hospital. Rommel steadfastly refused to eat, even when I warmed up the smelliest canned food that I could find. I knew that in his emaciated state, failure to eat was a death sentence so I tried every trick to get him to swallow a few bites. Nothing worked, so I called in Dr. Ott.

Every student had heard legends about Dr. Richard Ott: Head of Clinics, grandfathered member of the Veterinary Board of Internal Medicine, and developer of the first canine distemper vaccine. He was a larger-than-life figure who was universally respected by the faculty and feared by students. We guessed him to be in his mid-60's, but it was hard to tell; his face wasn't wrinkled, but craggy, like some mountain in New Hampshire in which pioneers imagined a likeness of a granite face. His hair was grey, but not in the white, kindly-old-man sort of way; his was wiry salt and pepper, cut to military length in a flattop haircut that had gone out of style in the 50's. While all of the other clinicians in the teaching hospital wore white smocks, his lab coat was ashen grey. Most of all, his attitude was intimidating; it felt like a chill wind preceded him thru the door of the sick cat ward.

Dr. Ott walked unceremoniously down the row of cages, asking if we had recorded the vital signs of each patient. Rather than ask the students on our team to explain our findings on each cat—his presumption of our ignorance was correct—he tersely explained that all of these cats had Feline Viral Rhinotracheitis and the best we could do is to provide supportive care and hope that they would recover enough strength to fight off the virus on their own. I ventured to ask whether the cats were in danger of worsening their infection by sharing the cramped cat ward with all the other germ-ridden cats. His dismissive gaze rested on me for only a second before resuming his explanation. I realized that the great doctor was being merciful, this being my first day among the feline patients. Everybody knew that Dr. Ott carried a red-inked rubber stamp that read "IDIOT", and when a student demonstrated their ignorance he would stamp their test paper—or their forehead, if it was during rounds—with bold scarlet letters.

The main question that Dr. Ott asked on each of the patients was "Is he eating anything?". Some of the cats had not eaten voluntarily in a month of hospitalization, and forcing food down these anorectic creatures was the most difficult part of their thrice-daily treatment regimen.

The sick cats were simply not going to eat and resisted our efforts to feed pureed baby food with a syringe. Dr. Ott warned that we would be unable to supply any significant amount of food by squirting it in their mouths with a syringe, so he told us that we would need to tube-feed each cat three times a day. Had we ever tube-fed a cat? When we all mumbled a negative answer he proceeded to demonstrate. He mixed a little lukewarm water into a jar of Gerber's strained egg yolk baby food and drew it into a 60cc

---

syringe with an oversize tip.   Fitting the end of a red rubber feeding tube over the end of the syringe, he lifted Rommel out of his cage with a tenderness that surprised us. With the cat sitting on the counter he deftly opened its mouth and smoothly slid the feeding tube over the back of the tongue and down the esophagus. He showed us how to squeeze in just a few drops at first; a weakened cat might not have the strength to swallow, causing the tip of the tube to go down the trachea with disastrous results. No coughing ensued, so Dr. Ott pushed the syringe plunger gradually until the full two ounces had been delivered to the cat's stomach. Withdrawing the feeding tube, he asked if we saw how it was done so that he didn't have to demonstrate it again. As we nodded our heads, we watched the cat rock back on its haunches, and with an impressive feat of projectile vomiting it launched the yellow food mixture forward, covering Dr. Ott's gray lab coat from the top button to the bottom hem. We froze, anticipating an explosive reaction from the Zeus of the Veterinary Hospital, known for his lack of both tolerance and humor. There was a brief pause before he stated in a matter-of-fact tone: "And that happens sometimes. Make up for it on the next feeding." There was a rush of wind as Dr. Ott pulled the door open and strode out of the room, leaving us to minister to the ward full of sick and suffering cats.

Half of the cats in the respiratory ward would never recover. Even though Rhinotracheitis is caused by a herpes virus (and anti-viral drugs were still a decade in the future), it was the bacteria that attacked the weakened lungs and provoked secondary pneumonia that caused most of the deaths that occurred among these patients. It was likely that some of the cats that died also carried Feline Leukemia Virus, a devastating HIV-like virus that cripples the immune system so that it cannot respond to infection. At that time there was no test for Feline Leukemia Virus, and FeLV continued to ravage the cat population for years, even after a new vaccine for Rhinotracheitis had controlled the respiratory disease. Eventually a vaccine for FeLV was also developed and lifestyle changes decreased exposure to the deadly virus, but even through the 1980s half of all cats that died from any cause carried the Leukemia Virus. If any of our patients had both Rhino and FeLV, their deaths were certain.

This first week in the Infectious Disease ward left us with a feeling of weary powerlessness, but at the end of the week we turned our dozen ill cats over to a new team of students. There was no magic bullet for the respiratory viruses, only "supportive care": Nourishment, liquids, and comfort. In the Infectious Disease wards we felt like frontier doctors from a century ago, who could only hold their patients' hands and spoon soup into their weakened mouths. But care and support are sometimes enough. The body has deep reserves of healing power, if we can buy enough time for nature to respond to the crisis.

At the end of the week Dr. Ott came by again, with instructions to make Rommel presentable. "Brush him out, clean up his face, and let him wander around the ward for a while to strengthen his legs. Rommel's owners are coming tomorrow to take him home." He had finally started to eat, and was on his way to a complete recovery, and I had played a part in saving a life.

23

Horse Sense

"Be careful, be careful, be careful": This advice described all aspects of working with animals. Sometimes it was the patient that we had to beware of; nobody is at their best when in the hospital, and even the most docile animal might lose patience and strike out with teeth, claws, or hooves. Sometimes we had to be careful to avoid harming the dogs, cats, horses, or cows for which we were responsible. We were still new at reading the scrawls of the attending doctors to determine what we should be doing during morning and evening treatments. Was "500mg penn/strep daily bid" some kind of tablet to force down the animal's throat, or was it an injection of milky white antibiotic? Did 500mg indicate the dose of pennicillin, streptomycin, or a combination of the two? Was 500mg the total daily dose to be given half in the morning and half in the evening, or was each twice daily dose to contain the full amount? We just hoped that we could read the doctor's handwriting, but many of the doctors were very impatient if we asked them to clarify: "What are you going to do when you are in practice next year? There won't be anyone to hold your hand or answer your questions then." Fearing a mistake, the four students on my team would constantly ask each other "What do you think he meant?"

Handling the animals for treatment put both the student and the patient at risk. Restraint class had allowed us to practice examining horses' legs and rectally palpating cows' abdomens, but our experience was confined to docile and cooperative animals that were kept for that purpose. Real patients, it turned out, did not find our fumbling attempts at drawing blood or opening mouths amusing, and they quickly sensed our inexperience and took full advantage.

After my experience in the sick cat ward, I was unsure of what awaited me on my first week in the large animal barn. Arriving in the large animal hospital at 6:30AM, our team searched for a clinician to instruct us in the duties of the week, but all we could find was another senior student. He told us just to go out to the stalls and check the treatment charts hanging on the wall.

In the second stall was a leggy reddish-brown Thoroughbred with a draining purulent lesion under its left eye. The instructions on the chart said to give an injection of penicillin, clean around the draining sore, and apply KRW liberally. The medical record indicated that the horse's name was Irish and he had been a racing horse with a modestly successful career on the track before developing a deep infection of the skull. We already knew that few horses ever made it back to the track once they were sick or lame, and their treatment often depended on the sentimentality of the owner or the generosity of the Large Animal Hospital. Fees were artificially low in the teaching hospital, and the doctors were reluctant to push a patient out of the clinic without resolving its problem. Whether this was a reluctance to admit defeat or a chance to provide the learning opportunity it afforded the students, a number of patients had been in the barn receiving treatments from anxious and inexperienced students for months at the school's expense.

Irish was already pacing around his stall when we approached, so we decided we should take him out and put him in the stocks for his treatments. He was an imposing animal, standing 16 hands tall (a hand is 4 inches, so that would be... you do the math—he was tall!) at the withers (where the neck meets the body

—the uninitiated might say the top of the shoulders). He seemed even bigger when he was agitated. His name fit him; his coat was the deep red of an Irish Setter or a pretty Irish lass's hair. We snapped a lead rope onto his halter and led him down the concrete corridor to the treatment room, where there were three open stall-like structures made of steel pipe and just wide enough for a horse to walk between chest-high rails and be tethered with its head sticking out the front end of the walk-thru restraint corridor . I gave Irish his pennicillin injection with barely a flinch (from the horse, that is); I knew how to hold the syringe needle-downward between my thumb and forefinger while thumping the heel of my hand on the horse's rump. After striking the horse with my hand three times to get him used to to being touched (apparently horses get hit on the rump regularly and learn to ignore it), on the fourth time I thrust the needle into the muscle and injected the white suspension. So far my first horse patient was behaving well, but horses who have spent their lives on the track have a skeptical relationship with their handlers and I knew his patience was being tested. When I began to clean up the draining sore below his left eye, Irish threw his head around in defiance. Fearing for both the horse's safety and my own (being hit by a moving equine head is more than painful), I attached a second lead rope and cross-tied his head to keep it motionless. He let me dab a large gauze sponge soaked in hydrogen peroxide around the wound, which had originally started from trauma that happened when his head hit the side of the starting gate during a race. I was far too tentative to be very effective, but I pronounced my cleaning adequate and searched for the KRW to apply.

Nowhere in the treatment room could I find the product prescribed. I didn't even know what KRW meant, although I guessed that it must be a topical wound medicine. By now one of the horse doctors walked thru the barn, and he chuckled as he pointed me to an unlabelled one-pound plastic jar filled with red goo. "That's Keuhn's Red Wonder, a concoction mixed up by one of the old horse docs. No one knows exactly what is in it, but Dr. Keuhn has been smearing it on horses for forty years. Oh, and you will want to wear gloves if you touch it." I scooped up a generous amount of the goo and made up for my inadequate cleansing attempt by smothering the wound with ointment. Now the crusty yellow drainage was covered by bright red paste (large animal vets seemed to like the theatrics of medicines that smelled bad, bubbled, or left stains that wouldn't wear off), and Irish and I both felt better as I detached his lead ropes and returned him to his stall.

Late in the afternoon the supervising veterinarian dropped by and asked casually how things had gone with Irish. By now I felt the confidence of my first successful equine encounter and replied, no problem. "That's good" the doctor replied; "When Dr. Keuhn was treating Irish last summer the horse lashed forward with a front hoof and broke Dr. Keuhn's leg." Confidence gone. Be careful, be careful, be careful. On succeeding treatments I approached Irish's head tentatively from the side, protected by the side rail of the stocks.

Most of this week of initiation into equine medicine was spent looking at legs. With the exception of colic (a life-threatening stomach ache that usually took a special colic team out on a stable call in the middle of the night under adverse weather conditions) and floating teeth (a crude dental procedure that involved sticking a long metal filing device into a horse's mouth to smooth down the rough edges that developed on the rear chewing teeth), all other horse problems occurred on the lower parts of the legs. We had already learned how to take x-ray pictures of the hoofed extremities, but now we were asked to examine the lame legs (which all felt pretty much the same to me) to familiarize ourselves with the feel of the bones and tendons that could support a half-ton of muscle as it raced around the track at 45mph. Why would anyone think that these slender bony legs would tolerate all that repeated impact?

Perhaps because of horses' long history as human transportation, the dysfunctions of the legs had folksy names (in the way that car owners would say their car has a blown transmission or a dead starter): Bowed tendons, bog spavin, founder, or the most mysterious of all, navicular disease. This last problem was difficult to understand, but seemed to involve inflammation around a piece of bone (called the coffin bone) buried (for no good anatomical reason) in the tendon that runs down the back of the foot to the hoof. This seemed like the equine version of the human plantar fasciitis, except people usually get over fasciitis after a year or two, and my impression was that horses with navicular disease rarely recovered. Many proud Thoroughbreds with illustrious racing histories retired and became riding horses for teenage girls when their legs became sore. Were those horses relieved or embarrassed, I wondered?

Every morning and evening, we spent several hours treating these limping horses with aspirin (pushing pills the size of your thumb down the horse's throat with a "balling gun"), ice baths, and old-fashioned liniments that burned if you got them on your skin (the old treatment of "firing" the skin over the sore area with a hot soldering iron had been outlawed, but the principle of "counterirritation" was still in vogue). These traditional treatments were starting to give way to therapeutic ultrasound, not because it was more effective, but because it had more of a scientific cache. An electrical box created high-frequency sound waves that were transmitted thru the horses skin with an appendage that looked like a hand-held shower head. After a water-soluble gel was applied to the handpiece it was held against the leg, moving constantly to avoid overheating the tissues and causing damage. Ultrasound therapy was not uncomfortable, maybe even soothing, but the treatment did involve close contact with the formidable legs. It was important to be alert to the horse's mood, watching for twitching of the ears; if the ears started to slant back toward the horse's neck, he was getting annoyed and caution was needed. The first rule of safety around horses was to either stand far away from the hooves or to stand right up close to the body so that the horse could not get any momentum behind its hoof if it lashed out. I preferred the "stand far away" option, but "stand up close" was necessary when treating the lame leg.

Ultrasound treatments typically lasted twenty minutes on each leg, so even starting treatments at 6:30 am I was usually late for the 8AM lecture class by the time the three horses under my care were led back to their stalls. If the staff veterinarians had to do the treatments themselves they may not have prescribed ultrasound therapy as often, but student help was free and plentiful.

When vet students were not occupied with the lower limbs of lame horses, there were more routine duties. Because the Large Animal Hospital was an indoor facility there was limited opportunity for exercise, so each patient had to be walked up and down the long concrete corridor for twenty minutes, morning and night. Even this task was not without its own fear factor. One of my walking duties involved a magnificent Appaloosa stud with an excess of energy and attitude. As I held the lead rope and walked him down the hallway, he would snort and challenge every horse that walked past, often rearing up on his hind legs with me desperately holding on to the lead rope and trying to calm him down. My anxiety about the horse hurting himself doubled when one of the horse docs mentioned that this stud was worth over a hundred thousand dollars. That these valuable animals were trusted to inexperienced students with little or no supervision was surprising, hardly soothed by the head of equine clinics, who simply repeated that "You'll figure it out."

Although there were more weeks in the horse barn to come, I was relieved to end the week without being kicked, bitten, or fallen upon. Next week's rotation had to be easier.

24

Disease by The Numbers

The week in the barn had been interesting in an old-fashioned horse-doctor sort of way. Even with modern treatments, an aura of the country horse doctor from early in the previous century hung over the stalls as a straw-and-manure reminder of where veterinary medicine had come from. Every examination or treatment was an opportunity for injury and disaster, and the trappings of scientific medicine were scarce.

It was with a sigh of relief that I entered the Clinical Pathology Lab for a week among machines with lights and beeps that could measure a sample of some bodily fluid and give an actual answer, a diagnosis of disease, a numerical value that told exactly what the patient was suffering from.

Preparing specimens in test tubes and inserting them into the lab machines soon lost its charm, however. I was left with plenty of free time to wander the small animal wards, looking in on the patients that belonged to the samples in the lab, imagining what a test result meant to the pet to whom it was attached. The alkaline phosphatase liver test that read ten times the normal value went with Otis, the Dachshund in Ward Two. He was wagging his tail and whining for food, attention, and more food, and he didn't look sick to me. His hair was thinning badly over his sides and his belly looked a little bloated, but he certainly looked better than his blood and urine tests indicated. Tomorrow we would test his cortisone levels, give an injection to stimulate the adrenal glands, and retest the cortisone levels later in the afternoon to see if his pituitary was overdriving the adrenal glands to cause the cortisone excess named Cushing's Disease. We were already nearly certain that we would find that Otis had excessively high cortisone levels; his symptoms were typical, and blood tests were being used to confirm a diagnosis rather than to randomly search for unknown abnormalities. Once confirmed, Otis could be treated with medication to partially destroy the overactive adrenals and he would return to normal. Fun detective work with little risk of death or disaster.

In the cage next to Otis was Heidi, a Schnauzer, and she did look sick. Heidi had eaten nothing and was hooked up to an IV running lactated ringers solution into her vein. "Sick" was all I could diagnose, but back at the Clin Path Lab I looked over her blood results and found that her urine was more dilute than normal and the urinary wastes, urea and creatinine, were three times normal. There it was, kidney failure, a diagnosis neatly wrapped up in definitive numbers from the chemistry machines.

But even blood tests don't always tell the true story. Jiggers was a Wire-Haired Terrier who had been referred to the veterinary school by a vet in Montana. Jiggers had been diagnosed by the home-town doctor with diabetes mellitus, the familiar "sugar diabetes". Diabetes is easy to spot from simple blood glucose testing: normal blood sugar for the dog lies between 80 and 120, and Jiggers had a glucose of 350. Diabetes, pure and simple. Except that she got worse when the vet had started her on insulin shots. The cheerful little terrier was scheduled for a glucose tolerance test Tuesday morning: The plan was to test her blood, give an oral sugar solution to see how high her blood glucose went, and then give insulin and repeat the test to see how the sugar level responded.

We took her first sample at 9AM that morning, which read 390; high, but not enough to cause the collapsing episodes that had prompted her to go to the vet in the first place. We squirted 30cc of a concentrated sugar solution in her mouth, which she willingly slurped down, and returned her to her kennel. We had planned to retest Jiggers' blood in an hour, but thirty minutes later she was wobbling on her legs, nearly falling into my arms as I opened her cage. I rushed her down the hall to the pathology lab to find an explanation, and the lab doctor looked a little puzzled. Repeating the blood glucose test took only 3 minutes, and it added to the mystery. Rather than going up with the dose of sugar water, the blood glucose had plunged to below 50, a level that can result in loss of consciousness and seizures. The drop in blood sugar was the opposite of what we had expected, so we skipped the planned injection of insulin, and considered what might cause the discrepancy. By mid-afternoon the glucose was back up over 400. Was Jiggers diabetic or not?

There is always an explanation for blood results, but sometimes a twisted narrative is required to reconcile the lab tests with the actual patient.

What about this explanation, the pathologist suggested: Jiggers' pancreas could have developed a tumor of the islet cells (the microscopic clusters of cells that sense blood sugar and release insulin when needed). Although these "insulinomas" usually crank out excess insulin constantly and keep the glucose levels dangerously low all the time, perhaps this dog had a tumor that overreacted and only produced insulin when prodded by an increase in blood sugar after a meal. The normal islet cells might have stopped functioning because they sensed the high levels of insulin produced by the tumor, so that once the tumor cells stopped secreting there wasn't enough insulin to keep the blood sugar normal. It seemed to be a strange scenario, but it turned out to be the truth. Jiggers was sent off to the surgeons for a surgical cure.

Do the tests, suggest an explanation, and do something about it. This was an invigorating glimpse into the sort of medicine that we might see on a television medical drama.

These moments of enlightenment were few, and most of the week was spent spinning down test tubes of blood, adding drops of reagents, and popping them into a colorimeter to turn the color change into a number. By the end of the week it was time to check in with the dead animal department.

Friday was a special day for students in Clinical Pathology. I was told to report to the Necropsy Room to observe the finale of the unsuccessful medical dramas of the week. Necropsy is the veterinary term for examining the dead body (necro=death, opsy=looking at) to find out what really happened. In human medicine they use the term "autopsy", which doesn't really make sense—(auto=self, opsy=looking at—looking at yourself?). Both pathologists in Post-Mortem had a certain haughty "see, I could have told you" attitude; the answers were easy, once you could see all the evidence spread out on a stainless steel table. The omniscient effect was lessened by the blood-covered rubber apron and the black neoprene rainboots worn by these final arbiters of death. Modern police dramas and murder mysteries have glorified medical examiners as all-knowing medical sleuths, but these veterinary pathologists looked more like workers in a meat-packing plant.

The Necropsy Room was packed with carcasses, some in the walk-in cooler, some disassembled on the table, and some delivered onto the tile floor by a forklift. Most of the dead bodies were livestock, brought in by farmers looking for a reason why their calves were wasting away or their four hundred pound pig had suddenly collapsed and died before it could be turned into pork chops. What the farmer feared most was that an infectious disease was discovered which would trigger a quarantine and potentially close down his farm. Hoof-and-Mouth, Brucellosis, Transmissable Gastroenteritis, Shipping Fever—the list of feared infections was long and all too familiar to the experienced agriculturalist.

The diagnosis that was most welcomed by the cattle rancher was "hit by lightening". A dead cow would be presented in the back of a pickup truck with the terse history of "He musta been hit by lightening, doc. He was fine just yesterday." Even the most naive veterinary student could see that the cow was emaciated, with yellow discharge oozing from its nostrils. And the weather had been clear for weeks.

The chief pathologist explained this favored diagnosis: Many farmers had livestock insurance that covered "natural disasters", including lightening strike, but not the "natural causes" of pneumonia, cancer, or the loose piece of wire that had been swallowed and perforated the stomach. Just give them the lightening diagnosis and they would be on their way home to collect the insurance check. The pathologist had a wry smile as he told us that he had at least one animal each week that had been supposedly killed by a bolt from the blue. Once he had even examined a carcass that had marks from the jumper cable clamps that had been used to create suggestive electrical burns. He had never seen one of the animals that didn't have some other cause of death.

Students were not expected to participate in the dismemberment of the dead animals, other than complying with the occasional request to help lift a sheep carcass onto the table. Mostly the pathologist grunted "see that white spot there on the liver", which we didn't, and he offered little explanation.

Few dogs and cats made it to the necropsy table. Most of the small animals that were treated in the WSU Veterinary Hospital were complicated cases referred from veterinarians in Seattle or the medium-sized cities across Idaho and Montana, cases that had been worked up so thoroughly that there were no unanswered questions that required a post-mortem report. I was relieved that neither Otis, Heidi, or Jiggers ended their week in the Necropsy Room.

The remaining lab rotation took me to the bacteriology lab, which seemed a world apart. It was housed in a separate building, not because of any fear of the germs that the bacteriologist grew on his agar plates, but because the link between the lab samples and actual patients was more removed, somehow less real and direct than the clinical path lab. A sample of some bodily fluid might yield the name of a microbe that was involved in an animal's disease, but the clinicians really only wanted to know what antibiotic they should use on their patient. Just send the culture and sensitivity report so we know that ampicillin will take care of it.

The bacteriologist never had the opportunity to meet the patients that supplied the samples, and somehow he didn't seem very curious about the live patients. Frequently no bacteria could be grown from the sample and the bacteriologist would write "no growth" and send his report to the clinician, his work done. But then what? The patient still had a problem, but it wasn't the bacteriologist's problem.

Veterinary medicine in the 1970s was still somewhat immune from the fragmentation that has caused much frustration in modern human medicine. Specialists do their jobs admirably within their own spheres, but their orbits may never cross those of other experts. Thus the cardiologist manages a patient's cholesterol and blood pressure perfectly but fails to see the respiratory problem or the hormone abnormality that underlies the patient's crisis. Human medicine is sometimes reminiscent of the parable of the three blind men and the elephant, in which each described the elephant only in terms of the part that he was feeling. Until the turn of the century veterinarians had control of nearly every part of their patient's health, treating a skin problem, removing a tumor, diagnosing a liver disease, and sometimes even running the needed medical tests in his own clinic. This allows a role for intuition: Sometimes the patient's appearance doesn't correlate with its lab tests or x-rays—the dog looks sicker than the bloodwork—and the doctor is in a position to take another look at the actual patient. Even when the clinical pathologists and bacteriologists generated pages of test results, I always liked to take a look at the animal.

After the abstraction of clinical pathology, necropsy, and bacteriology, I was longing for more real live animal action. Next was surgery, where swagger and prestige mixed with panic and disaster.

25

Under the Knife

Dr. Pettit and Dr. Robinette were as different as pickles and chocolate cake, but they were the heart of the Small Animal Surgery service. They performed state-of-the-art surgeries and allowed fourth-year students to observe their feats of surgical magic.

Surgeons carry the stereotype of lacking social skills and being arrogant; they say that surgeons don't have a God complex, but God has a surgeon complex. Dr. Robinette was so easy-going and genial that he didn't fit the surgeon's image, but Dr. Petitt was a different matter.

I had been warned about Dr. P, a brilliant doctor with an incendiary temper. He had the appearance of a mild-mannered accountant: Middle-aged, with light brown hair and wire rimmed glasses. But he had an anger-management problem that made working with him in surgery a tense affair. More than once he had flown into a temper when a procedure was going badly, cursing, throwing instruments against the wall, and, rumor had it, stalking out of the surgery room, leaving the patient in the hands of a startled intern. I had gotten off to a rocky start with him when Dr. P criticized the choice of instruments that I had purchased for my first surgery pack. He berated the fact that my needle holders incorporated a small pair of scissor-like blades behind the suture-holding jaws, a design used for speed and efficiency by many general practitioners. I shot back that I wanted to buy something that I could actually use in the "real world". It was a mistake to blurt it out, but he let it go. Despite the awkward beginning I enjoyed surgery rotation with Dr, P, since it was a chance observe a virtuoso perform complicated surgeries.

On my third day on surgery rotation a white stray cat (actually a barn cat, but no Palouse farmer would ever admit to actually owning a cat, or spend money on it) was brought into the hospital, the edges of both ears covered with bleeding crusts and lumps. Cats' ears are thin and delicate, and they sunburn easily in white cats that live out of doors. Eventually the ears develop Squamous Cell Carcinoma, a familiar type of skin cancer that eats away the tissue but is slow to spread to other parts of the body. What this cat needs, Dr. P said, was to have the ears amputated below the level of the cancers. He turned to me and asked if I would like to do the surgery so that we could find him a home. An actual surgical patient all my own? Of course!

After anesthetizing the cat I was unsupervised, and I spent most of the afternoon performing a fairly simple surgery, and it went smoothly. I cut across skin and cartilage halfway up the ear in a graceful curve so that he wouldn't look too disfigured. The ear is rich in blood vessels, so I had to stop frequently to tie off blood vessels with a strand of fine 4-0 suture each time a new skin artery started spurting blood.

All that remained was to sew the skin on the front and back of the ear over the exposed cartilage edge. I wanted my first patient to look really good, so I painstakingly placed tiny stitches spaced only a millimeter apart, instead of the three millimeter loops that would have made an acceptable result. Standing back, I thought that even the cat would think his cosmetic ear job was a sleek and aerodynamic improvement in his looks,. I checked in on my patient several times a day for the next week to monitor progress (actually, to admire my work), until a week later when suddenly he wasn't there. My first real surgery had found a new home where he could live inside, safe from the cancer-causing rays of the sun.

Most of surgical rotation was observation. Veterinarians are generally a self-sufficient lot, operating without surgical nurses or a posse of surgery residents hovering, ready to hand the surgeon a clamp or provide suction as an abdomen fills up with blood. Students were rarely invited to scrub in and handle instruments, but as Yogi Berra quipped, "you can see a lot just by observing."

The majority of the vet student's hand-on experience was provided by spaying and neutering animals from the shelter in Lewiston, Idaho. Since these dogs and cats were not encumbered by the liability of human owners, the surgeons simply turned us loose on these animals. Prepared only by our lectures in Junior Surgery class (now, where was that clean grassy space?), we were on our own to learn this most common veterinary surgery. In reality spaying can be tricky, even for experienced surgeons; A small one inch incision is made in the skin and muscle of the abdomen and a long hook-like instrument shaped like a shepherd's crook is inserted to retrieve the two horns of the uterus, earthworm-size fleshy tubes hidden among yards of intestine that make it impossible to see anything but guts. The two long horns of the uterus are pulled out thru the incision, but the attachments at the ovary and cervix ends are so tight that it is hard to reach the blood vessels that feed the organ to ligate them. If the clamps were placed across the end of the ovary a small remnant would be left and the dog would continue to come into heat every six months for the rest of its life, defeating one of the main reasons for the surgery. And if one of the ligatures slipped off after the connections were severed, the patient could bleed to death inside the belly.

In groups of three we took over the sterilization of a half-dozen homeless dogs and cats every Thursday afternoon, and over time we developed enough skill to confidently perform it when we took our first jobs in veterinary clinics, where spaying and neutering are still the bread and butter of the business.

On one Thursday afternoon my team was spaying our third dog of the day when we heard a commotion in the prep room, just on the other side of the surgery room door. Suddenly the door slammed open and Dr. P charged in, grabbed a scalpel bare-handed from our tray of sterilized instruments, and dashed back out without explanation. After the initial shock of the intrusion we followed Dr. P out into the prep room, where we saw a Great Dane lying flaccidly immobile on the prep table in a way that indicated it wasn't just sleeping. In one swift movement Dr. P sliced the scalpel thru the skin and muscle between the ribs and thrust his bare hands into the dog's chest to massage the big dog's heart, which had stopped suddenly during an x-ray procedure. We were riveted to the drama as Dr. P brought the dog back to life, got a pulse, and tersely said "Let's close him up", in a voice strangely quiet and calm. Then we got a fresh surgical pack and returned to our dog spay. Surgeons are by reputation confident, some would say cocky, and they are prone to overestimate their ability to solve every problems with a scalpel. But when action is needed, you hope there is a surgeon nearby. The next day I went into the post-op ward to see how the Great Dane was doing after his cardiac rescue, and he looked normal except the foot-long row of stitches on the left side of his chest.

Surgery is a strange art, relying more on action than on intelligence. The competent surgeon should understand the patient's inner workings, but the concept is simple: If it isn't supposed to be there, take it out, if it isn't supposed to be open, close it up, and if two things are supposed to be joined, put them together. The general considerations of surgery are easy to deduce:

If you cut it, it will probably bleed and you need to stop the bleeding. Know your anatomy so that you know where you are (a small structure like the adrenal gland can elude the surgeon, even when you know exactly where it is supposed to be, and you can get lost a half inch from your intended goal). And above all, be gentle; microscopic damage done to cells can impair healing and create severe complications.

I was at times overwhelmed by the powerful feeling of entering the body with my scalpel and holding a living organ in my hands. The warmth of the body cavities feels like life itself, reminding the surgeon that he is touching a force a billion years old but precarious and ephemeral in the moment. The pulse can be felt in the surrounding blood vessels, like a clock reminding you insistently that time is passing and every minute is precious. Most of all, surgery reveals disease made visible. The doctor who treats a kidney infection with antibiotics doesn't get to know the urinary organs on a shaking-hands basis. The closest the urologist gets is to see the urine produced by the kidney, while the surgeon sees first-hand the size, color, and consistency of the organ. And then he just cuts it out.

There is something energizing about working with your hands in a profession that requires so many layers of academic knowledge. Surgery has a feeling of carpentry about it, especially when repairing fractures or removing spreading tumor tissue. With the right tools, almost anything is possible.

26

Soft Tissues and Hard Problems

When Dr. Robinette was in the operating room, the atmosphere was relaxed. He was tall with a bit a surgeon's slouch. His black hair had a pronounced widow's peak, and he always had a wry, slightly amused smile and eyes that had a light-hearted appearance, even when his face was hidden with a surgical mask. He had just returned from spending six months at the University of Washington medical school, working with human surgeons as they pioneered the first human kidney transplants. While the techniques were being developed on dogs, by law a veterinarian had to be in charge of the operations while the MDs observed and kibitzed. Then when the first transplants were done on humans the veterinarian assisted the MD surgeons. Once the difficulties of the surgery were worked out, kidney transplants became the first widely used replacement procedures in humans. Although technically feasible, kidney transplants didn't find acceptance for dogs and cats until the last 20 years.

One obstacle (besides economics, the constant limiting factor in veterinary medicine) had been the ethics of taking a kidney from a healthy feline or canine kidney donor that could not voluntarily agree to the donation. When the University of California started doing kidney transplants, most of the patients were cats. Feline patients were less likely to reject the new organs, so the kidneys didn't have to match as closely as they did in dogs. The ethical issue of taking a kidney from a donor animal that was unable to give their permission was resolved in an unusually equitable way: Suitable donors were found among the inmates at a local animal shelter that had not been adopted. These cats were used as kidney donors, but with one condition: The owner of the cat that received the transplant had to adopt the donor cat for the rest of its life. True, the donor couldn't give informed consent, but it seemed a reasonable bargain, given the cat's options. Giving up a kidney in return for a new life and a new home is a trade-off that most of us would take. Perhaps out of appreciation for the shelter cat's contribution, these new families always became particularly attached to the donor cats.

The 1970's were a golden time to learn veterinary surgery. Human medicine had yet to become focused on high-tech surgery, instead relying on basic surgical skills to remove tumors, cut out sections of diseased intestine, and fix broken bones. These were all operations that a competent veterinary surgeon could do, and best of all, they didn't require fantastically expensive machines, large teams of highly-paid professionals, or custom-made prosthetic body partsnervousl. Improvements in basic surgical techniques opened up a wide variety of procedures that were economically viable for dog and cat patients.

Joint surgery had been nervously avoided because of infection problems, but improved sterility and stronger antibiotics opened the door to repairing torn cruciate ligaments and removing bone chips in the joints. Gas anesthetic machines were coming into use, which allowed surgery in the chest cavity to be done more safely. And improved soft tissue surgery techniques were being developed for some of the difficult problems faced by our patients.

The most popular surgery among student observers was a newly published technique called a Perineal Urethrostomy that Dr. R was perfecting. One of most common and deadly problems that affected male cats was a blockage of the urethra by a pasty mix of mucus and fine sand-sized struvite crystals. Once the urethra was plugged the bladder overfilled with urine and the kidneys stopped eliminating waste products.

The most urgent imbalance was potassium, an electrolyte excreted by the kidneys; if it increases to twice the normal level the heart simply stops. Cats would often die within twenty-four hours of a blockage, but if treated in time the obstruction could be flushed out and urine would start flowing again. Unfortunately, over half of these male cats had a recurrence of the problem weeks to months later. Dietary changes helped a little, but many cats died when another obstruction happened and nobody was around to rush them to a vet.

Surgeons always believe that they can find a cure to any problem. If the narrow male penis could be opened up to create a short, broad urethra like a female cat, then the mucus-and-crystal plug would be able to pass thru easily.

The idea was simple, but veterinarians had previously attempted the "sex change" operation with poor results. The urethra is small and delicate, and the healing process causes scar tissue that can close over the urinary opening, leaving the cat in even worse jeopardy.

A new technique was developed to split the penis lengthwise and suture it out to the side, overcoming this difficulty, and Dr. R was performing the procedure several times a week with excellent results. Each time he performed a perineal urethrostomy the operating room would be full of veterinary students, eager to learn the operation despite the "cringe factor" when the penis was split in two like a hot dog. Three days after graduation I had my first chance to apply a scalpel to a blocked tomcat. The cat was a stray, and would have died or been euthanized without treatment, so I had nothing to lose and no nervous owner concerned about complications. After closing hours at the first veterinary hospital where I worked, the boss let me stay late to attempt a perineal urethrostomy, with only my untrained sister-in-law as an assistant. Three hours later the patient was a new cat and I emerged with the confidence to recommend the surgery to clients whose cat suffered from recurrent blockages. Eventually I would be doing several cats a week myself with the knowledge gained at Dr. Robinette's surgery table.

In addition to innovative surgeries of the urinary tract, Dr. R was a master of orthopedic repairs. Nowhere was surgery more carpentry-like than in orthopedics. Broken bones (usually inflicted by moving automobiles) were a daily occurrence, and the surgical repair techniques often involved attaching bony parts together with pieces of metal. Sound engineering principles were critical; a stainless steel pin placed in the bone marrow had to be positioned so that the laws of physics did not allow movement or rotation of the fracture. Strands of stainless steel wire could encircle the bone to provide stability across a fracture, but only if they were applied along the lines of most stress. And the ends of the "cerclage" wire had to be twisted together just tightly enough: "One-quarter turn before the wire breaks" was the official standard.

Sometimes simply locating the broken ends of the bone was difficult. The femur bone of the rear leg, a common victim of contact with an automobile bumper, was hidden by a number of thick muscles which were swollen and hemorrhagic from the force of the injury. Placing a bone pin involved incising the skin, slitting the tough fascia covering of the thigh muscles, separating the appropriate muscle bundles (preferably parallel to the direction of the muscle fibers), and removing the clotted blood. The fractures always looked so accessible on the -x-ray, but seemed so far away when attempting to expose the ends of the bone. The atlas of orthopedic surgery, a slim green volume called Surgical Approaches To The Bones, was often laid open on a nearby table to help the surgeon find the most direct route to the site of the trauma without damaging anything important. Once the sharp ends of bone were located (trying not to puncture your surgical glove on a bony splinter), the ends could be lined up in their original position. Except there always seemed to be a fragment missing, like that old jigsaw puzzle that was always a couple of pieces shy after it had been assembled. Why didn't the x-ray show that the break wasn't clean? Aligning the bony ends seemed like a simple process, holding one end in each gloved hand and pointing them toward each other. But there were a lot of powerful muscles attached to the bone, and as soon as the bone breaks these muscles contracted in length and frustrated the surgeon's attempt to straighten the bones. At this point beads of sweat started dripping down inside the surgical mask, even when things were going as expected. When things were not going well, even the most mild-mannered doctor started using his "surgical vocabulary". After finally putting the bone together it had to be secured firmly enough that there would be not even the slightest instability or the bony ends would fail to heal together, resulting in a dreaded "non-union fracture".

At this point the surgeon had lots of accessories to hold the bone in perfect alignment: The simplest was an intramedullary pin, an eight-inch rod of stainless steel with a sharpened point on each end and screw threads cut into the first inch. This pin would be slipped easily into the marrow in the center of the bone, advanced smoothly across the fracture, and screwed into the lower end of the bone while being held with a "pin chuck" and handle which allowed the doctor enough leverage to drive the pin thru solid bone when needed. (Occasionally the chuck slips from the pin and the force of the surgeon's pressure would drive the sharpened back end of the pin into his hand—lesson learned). If a bone pin couldn't provide enough stability, several wires might be used to circle the outside of the bone, helping to hold any fragments in place. If pins and wires could not provide sufficient strength, a stainless steel place could be attached across the fracture site and secured with at least three screws on each side of the break.

The strength of the surgical implants had to withstand the forces that the animal would put on it, and it was a good bet that the patient would not listen to our warnings to avoid jumping and running for six weeks. By three days after surgery, many of our patients would put their full weight on the leg and bounce out of their kennel at feeding time. In six or eight weeks we could pronounce the dog healed. By then it was easy to forget that during surgery, when the splinters of bone refused to return to their original positions, the surgeon was sweating, cursing, and asking "Why did I agree to do this surgery". Ultimately, the healing process is up to the patient, and nature often helps out, even when our efforts fall short of perfection.

27

Hold Your Horses

Perhaps it was a conceit of every veterinary student that being a veterinarian would be just like being a "real doctor" (human MD), but with a wider variety of patients. Our medical knowledge covered patients that weighed as little as a one ounce parakeet or as much as a 1500 pound bull, had one stomach or four, or had five toes (dog or cat front paws), four toes (dog or cat rear paws), two toes (cattle, sheep, and pigs), or one combined toe (horses). Each species had its own set of viral infections, with important overlapping: Vesicular Stomatitis caused blistering lesions of the mouth and hooves in cattle, horses, pigs, and humans, while Hoof and Mouth Disease caused blistering lesions in cattle, sheep, and pigs, but not horses or humans, and Swine Vesicular Disease caused similar lesions in pigs, but not cattle or horses. Children have the confusingly named Hand, Foot, and Mouth virus with similar symptoms. It seemed obvious that human medicine just happened to focus on a single mammalian species that falls somewhere in the middle of the range of animals needing care. Dogs and humans are more similar to each other than dogs and pigs, and certainly share more characteristics than cats and chickens. Most medical and surgical procedures were so similar between the veterinary world and human medicine that veterinary students considered themselves just another kind of doctor-in-training.

There was one important part of our veterinary education that human doctors don't study in school: The skill of restraining their patients. Pediatricians might argue that obtaining a blood sample from a screaming three-year-old with his mother present is a daily challenge, but a class in Child Restraint is not part of the medical curriculum. Any ER nurse on a Saturday night faces dangerous physical difficulties, but their training is mostly on-the-job experience. Learning to restrain our patients was a basic requirement for all veterinary students.

The reality of hands-on experience started to become apparent with Animal Restraint class. Even though more than half of the students in our class were destined to treat only dogs and cats in their career, we took all of the same courses. A graduating veterinarian would be licensed (and presumably competent) to handle any animal presented, from a kitten to a Thoroughbred racehorse. Which meant that every student needed to know how to draw a blood sample from a Chihuahua, pass a stomach tube in a temperamental horse, or "set up" a three hundred pound ram (sheep are surprisingly uncooperative, as well as dirty and smelly, and the only way to get them to hold still for anything is to pull them up and backwards into a sitting position on their haunches).

No animal patient willingly submits to medical procedures, but they have different methods of resistance. Dogs try to escape first, using their teeth once their fear level reaches code red. Cats give plenty of warning with hissing and lashing with the front claws, but if heavy-handed restraint is imposed they may use their teeth (leaving tiny punctures which always become seriously infected) and rake with their powerful hind claws. Pet birds simply bite, and it is very unpleasant when an Amazon Parrot fastens onto your finger with its beak. As desirable as it was to avoid injury with small animal patients, instruction in small animal restraint was limited to techniques for drawing blood samples from dogs and cats.

Those small animal students that had worked in veterinary hospitals (which was almost a requirement for admission to vet school) already knew how hold a dog's front leg just at the elbow so that a doctor could slip a needle into the cephalic vein or position a nervous German Shepherd on its back to get an x-ray of its hips, but we still had to practice and demonstrate those abilities. The very fact that we called it "animal restraint" gives evidence that the techniques for handling the cuddly member-of-the-family pet were based on the farmyard techniques that had been established by the traditions of livestock doctoring from a century ago. Only recently have small animal veterinarians replaced "hold him a little tighter" with "let's let him relax a little and see if he will cooperate", a change that has been overdue.

Handling large animals was an entirely different experience. Every horse, cow, sheep, or pig we treated would be bigger and stronger than us and would be unlikely to choose to cooperate when we did something unpleasant, which included every task that the veterinarian performs. We learned how to use the squeeze chute for cattle, a narrow box into which a cow could be led, with barred walls on each side that could be tightened into a vise-like grip on the sides of the cow to hold it still (usually thrashing and bellowing) while an abscess was lanced or the mouth examined. We practiced "casting" a horse, a complicated procedure in which a sedated horse was looped with ropes that went over the withers, around the back hoof on the far side, around the neck, under the horse, and around the front hoof on the opposite side. Trussed up in this manner, a tug on the rope would (in theory) gently lower the horse onto ground on its side, at which point a full anesthesia could be administered for surgery.

The least humane technique in large animal medicine was the use of a twitch, which consisted of an ax handle with a loop of chain on the end. To control a horse for "floating" the teeth (using a specially shaped file to smooth off the painful rough edges of the molars when they grow and wear unevenly), the horse's sensitive upper lip is circled by the loop of chain and twisted tightly so that the horse can't move without creating more pain. I watched, but could not bring myself to try the technique, which seemed more appropriate to the enforcer in a gangster movie.

We learned all the techniques to handle any future patient, but the most important part of dealing with any animal was to read its body language, understand what it was thinking what it was going to do next. The mood of both cattle and cats could be read in how quickly the tail lashed back and forth. Dogs lowered their ears when fearful, while the laid-back ears of a horse signaled the it was getting annoyed. It was a good idea to pay attention to the messages of body language.

There is no substitute for experience and getting to know the animal that you will be treating. The large animal vet students had mostly grown up on ranches in Montana or dairy farms in the Okanogan area of northeast Washington, and they knew when to lean into the side of a cow at just the right moment to keep it off balance when it was considering swinging its horns at the person standing next to it. The horsemen (and one horsewoman, the most skilled equine handler in our class) understood how to watch the head and ears, when to step in closer, and when to step way back. Many of the small animal students had never touched a cow or sheep, and may have ridden a riding-stable horse only once or twice. When I was growing up in the Colorado Rockies my family had several horses, but I knew that my riding experience meant nothing when it came to holding a horse's head and using a "balling gun" to shove a large capsule down its throat. It struck me as strange that a professional school would take "city slickers" from the suburbs, draw a few diagrams about how to lift the powerful hind limb of a frightened horse, and then turn these same students loose with minimal supervision on stubborn farm animals and dangerous equines. It was a sink-or-swim, learn-on-the-job, rubber-meets-the-road introduction to the realities of handling animals for a living.

Restraining horses was the most dangerous part of veterinary education. This point was made one day when Mike, Leroy, and I were standing in the main hallway of Wegner Hall, where class pictures of each previous graduating year were displayed. Dr. Henderson, who had been the dean of the vet school for decades, came by and inquired if any of us were going into large animal medicine. When we replied in the negative, Dean Henderson said "That's good. Let me show you our past students that have been killed by horses since they graduated." He proceeded to point out at least one student in each class picture (including the previous June's group) that had made a fatal mistake while handling an equine patient.

Some of the rules of horse restraint were simple: Don't wrap the lead rope around your hand; better to lose control of the horse than lose your fingers. When approaching a horse from behind, give plenty of notice, both vocally and with a pat on the flank. Stay far enough away from the rear hooves to avoid injury when the horse tries to kick. If you aren't going to give the rear legs a wide berth, get right in close, so that the hooves can't develop momentum when they kick. In close quarters, don't get between the horse's chest and a solid object that might crush you. And remember that horses bite.

One thing that separates horses from dogs and cats is that they are prey animals in the wild, and survival depends on being part of a herd and overreacting to any sudden noise or movement. Freak out first, then look to discover that it was just a leaf blowing across the path. A rapid fear response is a basic part of the equine personality. And many times the horse's fear may be warranted.

Zephyr was beautiful, a slim dappled silver-gray, part Arab and part Quarter Horse. Her good looks were marred by the injuries that covered her head and neck. Her left eyelids were so swollen that she could barely see on that side. Her injuries had been sustained in a horse trailer incident; many horses object to being led into a confined trailer in anticipation of an uncomfortable two hour drive, and Zephyr had reared and pulled her handlers off their feet when they tried to get her into the trailer. They tried over and over to lead her in, becoming progressively frustrated and abusive (many horse people still insist that force and pain are necessary to get a horse to do what you want). As the fear level escalated, her panicked movements caused her to hit her head on the sides of the trailer. When she was halfway into the trailer her handlers smacked her hard on her rump and she reared up inside the narrow space, hitting her head on the roof, losing her her footing, and dropping to her knees as her head slammed repeatedly against the side rails.

I don't know how they eventually managed to transport Zephyr to the WSU Veterinary Hospital for treatment, but she was clearly traumatized and fearful of everything. That week I was assigned to the equine barn with Mike, Leroy, and Tim, and the first and last treatment on our agenda each day was to clean and treat Zephyr's wounds and administer a handful of 3-inch antibiotic and anti-inflammatory tablets.

Although many of the horses could be treated in their spacious box stalls, Zephyr was so apprehensive that we had to edge slowly into her stall, snap a lead rope onto her halter, and walk her out to the treatment area. Any attempt to touch the wounds on her face caused her to back away and rear up, so we decided to lead her into the stocks (a walk-thru framework of heavy steel tubing with a bar on each side and one above her head), where she could be restrained more safely.

Unfortunately, every time we would try to lead her between the chest-high bars she would balk fearfully and pull away, an understandable reaction considering the trailering trauma that she had been through. We were gentle but determined (and we were likely as frightened as she was), and eventually figured out that we could lead her past the stocks while shielding her view of them. Once we had her lined up we could get her to back up between the bars. This only worked if she didn't feel the rails on either side; if her rump bumped the bars she would rush forward and we would have to calm her down and try again. It took twenty minutes to get her securely in the stocks, but then she was calm and cooperative as we did her treatments.

This ordeal was repeated twice a day for the entire week, until Friday afternoon. Christmas break started as soon as the day's treatments were finished, and the attending equine doctor realized that none of us wanted to spend the last hour of our day putting Zephyr thru the long ritual of getting her into the stocks for treatment. "Let's make it quick and treat Zephyr in her stall", Dr Grant offered, "and I'll handle her for you." Dr. G was a consummate horseman who had a way with nervous animals and he understood how easily Zephyr could be spooked.

The box stall was 10' x 10' with a deep bed of straw on the floor. The walls were solid concrete up to five feet with another three feet of vertical steel tubing bars above which allowed us to watch how Dr. X handled Zephyr. He talked to the nervous horse softly as he approached obliquely, and he was quickly able to check the wounds and apply ointment without raising alarm. All that remained was to give the two large tablets with a balling gun, which consisted of a long tube into which the pill was inserted and a plunger on the back end to push the tablet down the throat when the balling gun was inserted into the back of the horse's mouth.

Dr. G held Zephry's halter in his left hand and started to insert the balling gun with his right, but the horse panicked and reared up on her hind legs. The straw under her feet slipped out, and Zephyr fell over backwards, but not all the way; she ended up sitting upright on her rump in the corner of the stall with all four of her legs flailing the air in front of her. Dr.G was pulled off his feet, but he still kept his hold on the halter, since it was better to be suspended from the horse's head than to be trapped on the floor in a small space with a storm of thrashing hooves. It seemed as if this moment stretched forever as we watched helplessly from outside the stall. We knew that at any moment the horse would fall over and the doctor would be crushed.

At the last moment Dr G released the halter, hit the floor with both feet, and sprang to the top of the stall bars in a single leap, an impressively athletic feat of self-preservation. Within a second Zephyr fell to the stall floor on her side and slowly got to her feet, unhurt.

Dr. G seemed unshaken as he brushed the straw from his legs. "Go ahead and take off, and have a good Christmas break", he told us calmly, "That's all for today."

28

Pig Patrol

Although every veterinary student was required to study all creatures, great and small, there was a distinct polarization between future large animal veterinarians, mostly rural students who had grown up on ranches and farms, and future small animal vets, mostly from cities and suburbs, who became interested in animal medicine by way of their own pets. And there were the horsey sorts from semi-urban areas where horses were kept for riding or racing.

There was one type of animal about which all students were equally ignorant: pigs. We had heard the lectures and memorized the major porcine diseases, but actual experience with pigs was confined to items on our breakfast plate. The experience we referred to as "Pig Patrol" would change all that. My weeks on pig patrol occurred during the snowy winter months, which were bad for driving but good for visiting pig barns.

A person could drive any highway across the state of Washington and never see a pig farm, but it turned out that there were a lot of small pork operations hidden among the hills and draws of the Palouse. Ambulatory duty involved a pickup truck fitted with various sized compartments loaded with any veterinary supplies that might be needed, a team of three or four students (I shared Pig Patrol with Mike, Leroy, and TIm), and a large animal clinician willing to drive all over Eastern Washington helping farmers with their problems. "Dr. Andy" Anderson specialized in pig farms, and he fit the part perfectly.

Dr. Andy was a large man with a bald head, a somewhat puffy face, and a body that barely fit into his oversize full-body overalls (although the zipper wouldn't close). He was always cheerful and enthusiastic, jolly even, which was a good attribute when driving a bunch of small animal students around the frozen winter landscape and up the rutted dirt roads that led to hidden hog operations. On our first morning, as we climbed aboard the ambulatory truck, we learned that the daily schedule was very important to Dr. Andy. "Let's go, we need to be out at the Jones' place by 8 o'clock sharp." "Why is that, Dr. Andy? Do they have a lot of pigs to vaccinate?" "No", was Dr. Andy's answer, "Mrs Jones makes the best blueberry muffins in the county, and they will be coming out of the oven just before the workers go out at 8." Things were looking up. "We need to be quick, though, because we need to be at the O'Sullivan place by 11:30." We shot him a questioning look, and he grinned and told us "The O'Sullivans set the best lunch spread anywhere, at least three types of pork, freshly baked bread, homemade jam, sweet potatoes dripping in brown sugar…". We caught the general drift of his commentary and climbed quickly into the truck.

The Jones' farm was a 40 minute drive, the first 20 over the icy highway and the latter 20 minutes (covering 2 miles) over a narrow road covered in snow deep enough to obscure the nature of the roadway underneath. As we pulled up to a worn-looking white farmhouse and climbed out (thinking of blueberry muffins), Dr. Andy turned and pointed to the left front tire of the truck, which had gone flat from bouncing over the icy road. He would go in and discuss the work to be done with Mr. Jones, while we changed the tire.

We looked at each other as dreams of muffins evaporated in the chill air. None of us cared to confess that our experience with changing tires was only slightly more than our experience with pigs, so we buttoned our coats against the wind and searched for the jack and spare tire. With our combined intellects and thirty years of college education we managed to change the tire in only forty-five minutes, at which time Dr. Andy strode out of the farmhouse, handed each of us a muffin, and told us to follow him into the pig house.

The first thing we learned is that the long low barns where pigs live are nice and warm—an instant relief after an hour in the snow changing a tire. The second thing that we learned was that the smell of the pig house is overwhelming in a way that must be experienced to be believed. I personally have always enjoyed the fragrant aroma of the manure of horses and cows, mixed with the smell of fresh hay into an honest barnsy olfactory ambience. This was not that smell. The odor was a physical presence that threatened to push us back out into the snow, but we persisted; perhaps we would get used to it, we hoped. The third thing was that it was dark in the closed barn, with only a single dim lightbulb hanging from a bare wire to light the rows of pens that housed several hundred pigs.

Our first task involved a large Duroc boar who stood sullenly by himself in a large paddock at the near end of the pig house. Judging from the depth of porcine feces, the pen had last been cleaned about the same time I had started veterinary school. Dr. Andy informed us that this four hundred pound specimen of porcine magnificence had been having diarrhea for three or four weeks, ("more likely three or four months", chuckled Dr. Andy) and the farmer wants to know why.

"First thing we need to do" Dr. Andy proclaimed, "is to take his temperature". Each of us carried one of the emblems of the large animal practitioner, a mercury thermometer attached by a string to a hemostat clipped above our overall pockct. "Harris, you go first." It didn't seem to be a question, but this was not something that I had been trained on. I shook down my thermometer and climbed over the two wooden rails of the pen. Even in the gloom of the pig barn I could see that the hog was coming toward me faster than I was approaching him. I took his manner to be menacing, so I retreated and surprised myself at how easily I could leap back over the fence rails. Dr. Andy just shook his head and motioned for Mike to show how it was done. Mike repeated the same sequence as I had done, and was followed in turn by Leroy and Tim. Dr. Andy gave us a look of mock disgust: "Don't any of you know how to take a pig's temperature?" Apparently we didn't, so Dr. Andy took out his thermometer, put his right foot up on the bottom rail of the fence, held the thermometer at arm's length and sighted the boar over his outstretched arm. "103 degrees", he stated with certainty. "That is how you take this pig's temperature". It was good not to be expected to know anything, I thought.

"Not sick enough to be viral diarrhea, so probably some intestinal bacteria. Go out to medicine cabinet in the truck and get a bottle of sulfa." Dr. Andy said. I could hear the big red hog making menacing noises just on the other side of the fence, so I hurried out into the cold to get the medicine.

We had one more farm, the Johanson place, to visit before lunch, at the O'Sullivans, but this time our patients were three-day-old piglets that needed iron injections. It was common practice to give iron shots to prevent anemia. The baby pigs were tucked cosily next to their mothers in small, tidy, warm pens, each with a "pig rail" about six inches above the floor around the inside of the pen. This rail kept the two hundred pound mama pig from rolling over and squashing one of the tiny piglets against the wall.

Although the little piglets weighed only a couple of pounds, they were surprisingly strong. And loud. Mike grabbed a piglet and held him between his legs. I jabbed him in his little hams with the iron shot while the little porker squealed at rock-concert decibels the entire time. After we finished with thirty baby pigs, it was time to head for the O'Sullivans'.

Lunch at the O'Sullivans was as good as advertised. On the farm, this was called dinner, the big meal of the day. There were at least a dozen steaming dishes on the table, and every one delicious in a "you've been out working in the cold all morning, you need your nourishment" sort of way. After three quarters of an hour we were warm and pleasantly stuffed, ready to head out into the cold for more porcine education. The O'Sullivans' pig barn was cleaner and better lit than our previous farms, and we were able to vaccinate three litters of pigs without incident.

After taking a turn up a wrong road which ended in a wheat field, we finally found the next farm. Dr. Andy reached into one of the back compartments and pulled out a couple of pieces of glass tubing, each about 4 inches long and and inch-and-a-half in diameter with a deep channel extending around the middle, and set them on the front seat. He offered no explanation for the strange piece of equipment, and we were too full of lunch to ask. We could see from Dr. Andy's face that the next problem was something more serious. We found that one of the sows had just given birth and had suffered a rectal prolapse. She was laying on her side when we reached her pen and her ten newborn babies were pushed off into one corner. A quick look revealed that three feet of her intestines were hanging out of her rear end, caked with wood shavings and feces. The straining of labor had pushed a small section of large intestine out of her anus, which caused her to strain and push harder, until a long stretch of intestine lay red and dripping in the straw.

"What do you think we should do?" asked Dr. Andy. The first unspoken answer that occurred to me was 'become an English major', but from the doctor's tone it was apparent that this was a routine occurrence and he knew just what to do. Occasionally a rectal prolapse will occur in a dog or a cat, and the veterinarian just needs to clean and lubricate the protruding tissue, gently push it back into the anus (strangely like putting toothpaste back in a tube) and place a "purse-string suture" around the anus so that it can't pop back out. But the prolapsed pig intestine lying on the floor of the pen was so soiled, covered with straw, and discolored, that it was clear the tissue had lost its circulation and the gangrenous stretch of intestine would die and fall apart, even if we could get it back inside the sow.

Dr. Andy looked directly at me and asked "This mama pig will die and her babies might not make it if we don't do something right now. What are you going to do?" I glanced at my teammates for a hint, but they were still looking down in alarm at the momma, the prolapse, and the baby pigs in the corner. "Does this have something to do with those glass tubes on the dashboard of the truck?" I guessed. "Right you are. We will make a pig doctor out of you yet" Nope, English major, I muttered. I should have started writing my Great American Novel right then, but instead I ran to the truck to get the glass tubes, which it turned out came in three different sizes.

"This is simple, so I will explain it to you as you do the procedure". What? "First, get in the pen and kneel right behind the sow. But try not to step on the prolapse", he said with a grin. "Now take one of these glass rings and slide it up inside the intestine." I picked the middle-size tube, since for all I knew she was a middle-size pig, and followed his instructions. Once I found the opening at the far end of the prolapse, the tube slid in easily and I milked it up toward the sow's anus. My patient was still recumbent, too weak to object to the violation that she was undergoing. "Now, push the tube as close to her anus as you can, and tie this piece of string tightly on the outside around both layers of intestine until the tube won't slide any more." Hands trembling, I cinched the piece of string (not sterile suture, but a regular piece of string) as tight as I could. "Tighter". Ok, I pulled it even tighter than I could. "Now the easy part: Take this knife and cut off all the intestine beyond the tube and push the tube inside." Really? "There you go. The intestine heals quickly, and in a few days the layers of intestine will heal together and she will pass the glass tube. She'll be fine." I looked at the rest of the team, who were staring in disbelief. "Next time it is your turn" I told Mike, trying to sound as casual as I could.

"Let's go", Dr Andy said, "We have one more stop before we are done, and it looks like more snow is moving in."

There was no conversation in the ambulatory truck, just contemplative silence as we drove through the hills to the two-lane highway. After twenty minutes we pulled up to a shabby tavern at a crossroads marked "town of Yellow Dog", which does not appear on the map. Dr. Andy motioned us to get out of the truck and we followed him into the bar. The three locals seated at the bar looked at us with a combination of curiosity and suspicion. At the time we thought that it was because several of us had long hair, or that no one under the age of fifty had ever come into the establishment, or that we were strangers. Now I realize that it was our smell; the pungent aroma of the pig barns made an entrance before we did, and even these old farmers with manure on their boots thought we smelled terrible. We did, and we wore it as a badge of honor.

After Dr. Andy bought us each a beer (I didn't drink mine, but I accepted the gesture of approval) and told us that we were now pig doctors we climbed wearily into the truck and drove back to Pullman.

179

Although I knew that I would never have to treat a pig in my veterinary career, there was a certain feeling of being initiated into the mysteries of porcine medicine. My sense of accomplishment evaporated when I opened the door to our little apartment on South Fairway. "WHAT is that smell?" Terri exclaimed; "If you are going to come inside, you need to take off all of your clothes and get in the shower!" "And that coat of yours can't come in the house, no matter what. You will have to leave it out on the porch." That was the most painful part. I had a split cowhide coat with fake sheepskin lining that I had gotten when I was 16 years old, with western styling that suggested that I should be wearing a Stetson and galloping across the prairie. It had been my favorite for eight years, and now it had to spend the night in the snow hanging over the wooden railing of our porch. Terri was right, of course, but leaving this proof of my new country vet status outside reminded me that I was really just a guy with a smelly coat.

The following days brought more of the same. Dr. Andy knew every good farm table in Whitman County, and I gained five pounds during my two weeks on Pig Patrol. Most of our duties became routine: giving iron injections to piglets, vaccinating older piglets, and castrating young pigs at six weeks of age. Removing pig testicles was farm surgery, and efficiency was paramount. One of us would grab the piglet by both hind legs and hold it upside down with its shoulders between our knees. At this age the little porkers weighed ten pounds and were surprisingly strong. Sterility consisted of wiping povidone iodine across the scrotum (which didn't really kill all the skin bacteria, but the orange stain it left suggested some protective power). Then I took a scalpel with a hook-shaped blade and cut thru the skin and into the testicle. I pulled it thru the incision and severed the spermatic cord, letting it retract back into the hole in the skin. Sometimes one of the little pigs would have a hernia, an open connection between the scrotum and the abdominal cavity. For these we would inject a local anesthetic and place a few sutures to hold the hernia closed until it healed. Before letting the squealing patient back into the pen to complain to his littermates, we would give vaccinations for the common porcine diseases.

At one time herds of pigs were more important to Washington State's agriculture than they are now. Even the great Dr. Ott, when he first became a veterinarian, had been a farm doctor, treating pigs as well and sheep and cattle. When asked why he had switched to dog and cat medicine, he told this story:

One of the most contagious and feared livestock diseases was (and is) Foot and Mouth Disease. The virus spreads in disastrous epidemics affecting all sorts of split-hooved animals: pigs, cattle, sheep, and goats. The economic losses caused by the virus are so severe that if a case is diagnosed on a farm every animal must be killed and buried to prevent the disease spreading to other farms. The farm will then be quarantined for months. No livestock can be sold or moved within the entire county. There is a vaccination for the disease, however, and Foot and Mouth Disease has been completely wiped out in many countries.

Modern vaccines use a weakened virus that is incapable of causing disease. In the 1930s, however, vaccination was performed by giving 1 cc of virulent virus. while simultaneously giving 10cc of antiserum to kill the live virus as soon as it entered the animal's system.

One of Dr. Ott's tasks during his farm vet days was to vaccinate a herd of pigs in Walla Walla against Foot and Mouth Disease. But this was his first herd of pigs, and he mistakenly gave 1 cc of the protective antiserum and 10cc of the live virus.

As Dr. Ott told it, three days later, his telephone leapt off the wall and caught on fire. The entire herd of pigs had come down with Foot and Mouth Disease from the virus/serum mixup;

the herd was wiped out, and all livestock production in the entire county was shut down. The next day Dr. Ott became a small animal veterinarian.

I enjoyed my first week on pig patrol (except for the smell), and when Dr. Andy told us that he had us for another few weeks (due to the illness of the bovine ambulatory vet, which was to be our next rotation), I wasn't disappointed. We drove around the wintry Palouse countryside, shared the cooking of the farm wives, and enjoyed the warmth of the pig houses. But finally our traveling pig adventures came to an end. Terri had still exiled my "pig coat" from the house, and with the end of Pig Patrol, I was sadly required to burn my favorite coat. We gave it a proper funeral, and sent it off to the garbage with a blueberry muffin to accompany it into its afterlife.

Interlude 5

Christmas break was coming up, and I had experienced all sorts of animals; dogs, cats, horses, cattle, sheep, goats, pigs, even the live cougar that the college kept as a mascot. While not becoming expert, I was no longer completely ignorant about the handling of these living beings. But I was about to face the most intimidating challenge of my vet school experience.

Terri had found out that she was pregnant the previous spring, and now it was time. Having our baby was complicated because her gynecologist (an older Hungarian doctor who had also been her pediatrician when she was a child) practiced in Bellevue, three hundred miles away. The hospital in our college town was no place to have a baby. She was due to deliver in early December, so we decided to have her stay at her parent's house in Bellevue rather than return to Pullman after Thanksgiving. I was nervously hoping that the baby would wait to be born until the beginning of Christmas break so I could get there in time; the current practice of letting a father skip work or school just because his wife was delivering had not yet occurred.

December 23rd came, Terri was three weeks overdue, and still no hint of when the baby would be born. She was getting tired of waiting and restless from staying with her parents at a stage in life where she didn't need anybody giving advice. Her doctor was extremely strict about limiting weight gain; theories about the-more-weight-the-better and don't get-fat-during-pregnancy have seesawed back and forth for decades, but her doctor was solidly in the latter camp. Dieting was hard even in normal times, but with stress and a growing baby it was particularly difficult for her. (Her weight after delivery was the lightest she had been since 7th grade, so her worry was overrated).

Christmas came and went, each day looking forward to that adrenaline-filled announcement, "I think you had better take me to the hospital right now." The doctor reassured her that just because she was three-and-a-half weeks overdue was no reason to panic, and that babies come when they are ready. Perhaps he was just Old Country and Old School, but there was nothing we could do other than return for doctor checkups every few days. The date was approaching when I would have to return to Pullman, leaving Terri to fend for herself as the event drew near. On the evening of December 30th, three days from when I had to leave for school again, her anxiety got the best of her, and she begged me to take her to Denny's for a hot fudge sundae. It couldn't hurt, although she had another doctor checkup and weigh-in the following morning.

We sat in a booth at Denny's and ordered two large hot fudge sundaes with everything on them. Then we noticed that the gynecologist's nurse was having dinner in the next booth. Pleasantries were exchanged, but now Terri had a new cause of anxiety: she would have to face the calorie police in the morning and the nurse might reveal her indulgence.

Three hours after our sundaes, she finally told me that we should think about going to the hospital, no hurry, but contractions every five minutes. I wisely abstained from asking if it might just be the hot fudge talking, and by 4AM New Years Eve we were in the admitting room of Overlake Hospital.

Twelve long hours of contractions every five minutes, and still no progress. A shot of oxytocin to speed things along, still nothing. I had used up all the quarters that I had brought for the pay phone to give updates to our parents, saving one for the actual moment of delivery, so we were out of communication with family. Waiting. At least, we thought, if she waited until after midnight of the New Year she might have the first baby of 1974, which traditionally came with some gifts from local businesses. Midnight, still waiting, while another obstetrician brought his patient in at 11:30, induced her, and at 12:05 I could hear him on the phone at the nurse's station calling the newspaper to report the first baby of the New Year. Still waiting, until 4AM New Years Day, when our son was born in the usual way.

This was the first generation of fatherhood in which men were allowed in the delivery room. I had seen baby pigs born, watched a canine C-section, and held a cow's head as a vet inserted his arm up to his shoulder to reposition a calf, so the birth process was no mystery, but my feelings were completely different.

Our lives changed immediately. To be fair, Terri's life changed more immediately than mine, as I had to leave two days later to return to Pullman, leaving Terri with the baby and her family until I could return to rescue her and our son in three weeks.

Knowing what to do with a little one once he was in my arms was scarier than taking a bull's temperature. Caring for an infant in a poorly heated apartment with no one around who knew anything about babies brought a new kind of anxiety. I understood the feeling of being responsible for another life, but this was something more, and it changed me. Rather than "taking responsibility" for what happened to our son, there was now a feeling of protection, of anticipating the multitude of dangers and deficiencies that could happen. Doctors promise to do no harm, an impossibility in either child-rearing or in medicine; it isn't that we have to take responsibility for mistakes, but rather that the results of any mistake, however small, are unthinkable. From the moment of our son's birth, it was unalterably imprinted on me: This life is entrusted to you, and you can't let anything happen to it. After this I viewed my patients in a different way as well.

For the first time I understood my mother, who was a famous worrier, well beyond the "wear your coat or you'll catch pneumonia" sort of cautiousness. I realized that worry is more than "today's mouse nibbling on tomorrow's cheese"; it meant anticipating every possible adverse event that could happen, imagining the worst, and placing yourself between harm and your loved one (or your patient).

My psyche may have been changed, but Terri bore the daily responsibility for the next five months, as my vet school duties didn't slacken. She was cloistered in our South Fairway home trying to keep our baby warm and fed. For the first three months the weather remained snowy and frozen, conditions that kept our old car from moving at all. The only time that Terri could get out of the house was on Sundays, when we made the trek to the laundromat and grocery store. Sometimes she would brave the weather and walk down to the vet school where we would wander through the large animal barns with our baby (who became severely allergic to horses as he grew up; maybe that was my fault as well?). With graduation in sight, there wasn't time to think about anything but caring for our son and completing our journey. It felt as if we were being carried forward by a river, floating at times and sinking at others, just looking for open water ahead.

29

Cows and Nitrogen

Winter still gripped the Palouse as the new year started, and with it came three weeks on the ambulatory truck that provided out-patient cow care. While Pig Patrol had the advantages of warm pig barns, sumptuous farm breakfasts, and permission to be ignorant about our patients, bovine ambulatory was outside in the elements, the patients were wily and uncooperative, and Dr. Bracken stern and intolerant.

The first ambulatory trip of the new year took us just across the state line to the University of Idaho in Moscow. The object of our trip was to check in on a Herford steer with a rumenostomy. The Animal Science department at the U of I was studying ways to meet the nutritional needs of cattle more cheaply. In order to do this, they needed a convenient way to sample the bovine rumen, the huge fermentation vat that serves as the cow's "first stomach". The rumen measures three feet by two feet, and takes up most of the cow's abdomen. Everything the cow eats joins the soupy mixture in the rumen, where bacteria break down the otherwise undigestible cellulose of grass and hay that the cow chews and swallows, And then regurgitates, chews, and swallows. Again and again, until the mixture is sufficiently "cooked" into a nutrient sludge that moves on to the next three stomachs and into the small intestine, where the carbohydrates, fats, proteins, vitamins, and minerals are absorbed and distributed to the hungry tissues. But one nutrient outranks all of the others: Protein.

For most animals and plants, nitrogen is like gold. Amino acids (literally, organic acids of nitrogen) are the building blocks of all of the enzymes, hormones, and proteins in the body. But nitrogen in its organic forms can't be produced in the body by animals (or most plants). Some plants (such as alfalfa, peas, and beans) solve this problem by hosting "nitrogen-fixing" microorganisms in nodules on their roots, and then using the amino acids from their captive bacteria, while other plants rely upon organic nitrogen left behind by those plants (or added to the soil as commercial fertilizer). Most animals have to find protein to eat to satisfy the nitrogen craving: carnivores find it in the flesh of other animals, while herbivores find second-hand nitrogen in plant protein. But plants tend to keep their nitrogen sequestered in cells with tough walls of cellulose. Cellulose is what gives wood its hardness and rope its strength. The purpose of the rumen is to liberate the nitrogen trapped in plants by allowing bacteria to break down the cellulose, create bacterial proteins and amino acids, and then—the cow digests the bacteria and uses their hard-won nitrogen.

Following this line of thinking, scientists look for other less expensive sources of nitrogen that bacteria can turn into protein, and to study this they need frequent sampling of the rumen to analyze the contents and the types of bacteria that feed on whatever goes into the rumen. For this, you need a rumenostomy.

The rumenostomy was a permanent "window" into the rumen. In a simple surgery, an incision was made thru the skin and muscles on the side of the cow's abdomen, the wall of the rumen was brought up to the opening, incised, and sewed to the skin in a circular window. A round frame with a swinging door was fastened to the opening, which is six inches in diameter, just large enough for a curious person to stick their entire arm all the way inside to take samples.

The WSU Veterinary School provided medical service for this experimental cow and others, which meant that every few weeks Dr. B and students would drive over to Moscow to clean the edges of the rumenostomy and make sure that the plastic window was secure. This gave students a good opportunity to look directly inside the digestive system while the steer contentedly munched on breakfast in his stall.

I unhooked the rumenostomy cover and looked inside. The sheer size of the first stomach is impressive; "There is sure a lot of rumen there", I quipped. The cow turned its head to look at me with an expression that seemed to say "Really? I've never heard that one before".

This cow was part of an experiment to see whether cows could be fed cardboard as a source of nitrogen for the cow's protein-producing microbes. Cardboard is cheap and could be ground up and mixed with other cattle feeds as an inexpensive hay substitute. The cow didn't offer any opinions about the taste. I scooped out 500 ml of the green-ish brown rumen contents for the lab and the Dr. B checked the rumenostomy for any leakage or infection around the opening. Then he instructed one of the other students in our group, Gary, to lead the cow to another barn on the other side of a wide fenced alleyway. Gary was as inexperienced as I was in handling cows, so he wrapped the halter's lead rope around his right hand to make sure he had control as he started to walk the animal across the alley. When the cow got into the middle of the alley it noticed the inviting snow-covered pasture at the end of the lane and turned and galloped toward the opening and freedom. Gary couldn't stop the lumbering bovine, and ran behind as the cow headed for freedom. Once they reached the open pasture, the cow picked up speed. Gary didn't let go, because he didn't want to be the student who let a valuable research animal escape, and also because—he couldn't let go of the lead rope. In animal restraint class we had been told never to wrap a lead rope around our hands, and now the reason became clear. Gary ran as fast as he could, but the lumpy snow tripped him as the cow sped up. In a moment he was flat on his stomach being dragged across the icy pasture with his face plowing a furrow in the snow. After a hundred feet the cow came to a stop and nosed around the ground, looking for a tuft of something under the snow that didn't taste like cardboard. I looked at Dr. B, whose normally stern countenance showed a hint of amusement as he walked up to the animal and led it back to the barn.

The incidence broke the ice with Dr B (in a manner of speaking), and on the drive back to Pullman we asked about other cattle-feeding experiments. They had tried feeding just about anything that could be converted into protein by a ruminant: sawdust, corn stalks, wheat straw.

They simply needed to find the right bacteria to turn undigestible material into protein. Some of the animal scientists thought even farther outside of the (cardboard) box; animals need nitrogen in their diet, but they also eliminate nitrogen-containing waste products through the kidneys. Why not recycle all the nitrogen that leaves the body as urea, they thought? What if they recycled the cow's own urine by creating a surgical detour from the bladder to the rumen, so that nitrogen in the urine could be processed back into protein by the cow's microbes. What happened, we wanted to know? The results were a disaster; even though urea can be turned into protein in the rumen (and purified urea is added to some cattle feed), urine also contains lots of other toxic substances that the body needs to get rid of, and when urine was recycled rather than eliminated those toxins built up and sickened the cows. There is more going on inside a cow than meets the eye, even with a window to see thru.

The Palouse wind had blown most of the snow off the hills the following week, when the ambulatory truck was called out to a farm near the town of Dusty. Dr. B seemed even more serious than normal as we drove an hour along a winding country road. He wouldn't tell us what awaited us at the ranch, but as soon as we turned up the draw we knew. The hillside was littered with the bodies of thirty-five cattle; the only live animal in sight was a scrawny calf that was huddled by the barn. The scene looked like a battlefield with no survivors, and we had no clue what could cause such devastation.

Dr B handed each of us a sharp necropsy knife and told us to go out into the field and open up one of the carcasses to see if we could tell anything while he went to talk to the rancher. We had all observed post-mortem examinations in the vet school's stainless-and-tile necropsy room, but none of us had ever performed the task. As first we were tentative, trying without much luck to pierce the hide and abdominal muscles. The wind seemed to blow more bitterly and we abandoned any attempt at finesse, stabbing away until the cow's bloated belly was laid open and chocolate-brown blood oozed out over our shoes. Does anyone have a clue, one of us asked? The organs looked normal enough, with no sign of pneumonia, liver disease, or hemorrhage. The only finding that was out of place was that the blood was chocolate brown and still liquid, with no sign of clotting.

When we had studied the lists of diseases in large animal classes, there was only one disease that featured blood that wouldn't clot: Anthrax. All four of us froze: there was no avoiding it, we had just exposed ourselves to one of the most feared and deadly infectious diseases, a plague that attacks humans as well as most other mammals.

Anthrax had caused intermittent mass deaths in grazing animals for many centuries. The bacillus that causes the infection produces a spore which is resistant to drying, freezing, or time. If an animal dies of anthrax there is no way to decontaminate the soil and when a flood or excavation brings the spores to the surface every animal that grazes the pasture will rapidly sicken and die. We walked up to the barn, where Dr B was examining the forlorn calf. We think it might be anthrax, one of us said in a voice that was meant to be calm and knowledgeable. Dr B didn't turn around, he simply said it wasn't anthrax, but nitrite toxicity.

How could an entire herd of cattle be poisoned? Had someone done it intentionally? No, he later explained, the rancher had gotten a bad load of hay. In Eastern Washington there were certain combinations of growing conditions that caused hay to accumulate nitrites from the soil, and there was no way to recognize a load of bad hay. This was the dark side of nitrogen. Nitrite kills silently, and likely painlessly, by turning the red oxygen-carrying hemoglobin in the red blood cells into brown methhemoglobin. The dark color was due to methhemoglobin's inability to bind oxygen, causing the tissues to suffocate and the animal to die.

The calf had also been mildly poisoned, but it was still nursing and only nibbled a small amount of tainted hay. There was a treatment for the survivor, which seemed as bizarre as the poisoning itself. Dr B instructed us to go to the truck and get a 250ml bottle of methylene blue, an IV tube, and a needle. We were familiar with methylene blue; it was intense purplish-blue stain that was used in the laboratory to stain tissues on a microscope slide so that the inner features of the cells would be visible under the microscope (and also used in serious college hazing). As Dr B hooked up the IV and started running the stain solution into the calf's veins, he instructed us to look at the whites of the calf's eyes. Within minutes the whites turned a deep shade of blue, an interesting if alarming sight. Methylene blue separates the methyl molecule from the hemoglobin, allowing oxygen to once more be carried to the animal's tissues. Dr. B warned the rancher that the calf's urine would be bright blue for a few days, but it would survive. The entire load of hay that the rancher had purchased to last the winter would have to be burned, however. As we drove past the hillside of carcasses we wondered what the rancher would do with the bodies: Dig a mass grave with a bulldozer, or simply let them decompose where they were? We also realized that the rancher would probably be bankrupted by the loss of his herd; keeping cattle was economically risky at best, and the threat of death and disease were always present.

30

Congratulations, You're Pregnant

During the final week that our group was on ambulatory Dr B was ill, and Dr. Mickelson was assigned to drive the truck with our group. Dr M was mostly a horse guy, but there was one thing he truly loved: pregnancy checking cows. "Preg checking" was an economic necessity for the rancher, a steady source of income for large animal veterinarians, and a bread-and-butter skill that any new veterinarian would need if they wanted to work in ranch country.

In theory, the procedure could not be simpler: The highly trained doctor of veterinary medicine inserts his bare arm into the cow's rectum up to his armpit and feels for the uterus, which rests below the colon. The hand is moved up and down to feel for a calf's head. You can't actually move your fingers to feel, so a downward patting motion is used, called "ballotment", and if there is a baby cow in the uterus your hand will feel it bounce downward when touched and rebound again. The feeling is like dribbling a basketball under water. If the cow is declared pregnant, then it is turned loose to pasture; if it is not pregnant, it goes to the slaughter house. The rancher can't afford another year of feeding an animal that will bring no financial return. As a novice palpator, I felt like a judge who has the power of life and death, depending upon what I imagined that I felt inside the cow.

Dr M was eager for the day's work, one hundred head of cattle to preg check and vaccinate, what could be better? We were more skeptical, not only because our only experience at rectal palpation was three years ago in Large Animal Anatomy class, but also because it was twenty degrees outside, with wind blowing fine snow sideways. The members of our group agreed to take turns: one would hold the cow's head, one would vaccinate the cow using a Ranch Record syringe gun that delivered a dose of serum each time the handgrip was pulled, and the remaining student would do the actual palpation.

On this day our group included Leroy, a fellow dog-and-cat guy, and Reed, who came to veterinary school with the sole interest of treating reptiles. Reed was almost reptilian in his manner: he was tall and skinny, and he moved with reptilian slowness. Reed was assigned to do the pregnancy checking first while I vaccinated the cows. We trusted that Leroy would restrain the cows as we did our part, but these were range cattle being checked in a snowy barnyard corral, not tired old milk cows tied in convenient stalls. Reed had long arms, but moved so slowly that we stood shivering next to the first cow for almost 15 minutes before Reed proclaimed that the cow was pregnant—he thought. The second cow took only ten minutes to receive her verdict, but it was already clear that we would never make it through a hundred cows and get back in the warm ambulatory truck before we froze to death. I handed Reed my Ranch Record syringe and suggested that he vaccinate while I did the preg checking. Leroy seconded the idea, and I stripped off my coat, unzipped my standard-issue veterinary overalls and folded them down to my waist, and pulled a thin transparent polyethylene fingers-to-shoulder obstetrical glove over my freezing bare arm. The cow eyed me warily as I sidled up to her rear end; she was a range animal, and had contact with humans only a few times a year. Cupping my fingers into what I hoped was an efficient shape I pushed into the cow's rectum. The anal sphincter offered a lot of resistance, but once in the colon I could slide my whole arm inside the cow. The first thing I observed was that the anal sphincter was surprisingly strong, compressing my upper arm painfully. The second thing I noticed what the it was warm in there. In fact, it was the only part of me that was not freezing. Without pausing to enjoy the warmth, I patted my fingers downward, hoping the the head of a calf fetus would feel as I imagined it would. After a few tries I felt something rounded but not as firm as I expected, right under my fingertips. It could have been the bladder, but I chose to identify it as part of a fetal calf, pronounced the cow pregnant, and withdrew my arm. The third thing I observed was that fresh cow manure is steamy, but it doesn't smell as bad when it is twenty degrees outside.

Reid pulled the trigger on the vaccinating gun and Leroy let the cow loose. My second cow felt the same as the first, but this time Reid stabbed it with the vaccine while my arm was still inside, and the animal gave a jerk and a half-hearted kick. It took only seconds to declare the cow pregnant and move on to the next one. The third cow was the same as the first and second. Good so far, I thought, I'm getting the hang of this. The fourth cow was different; it was a smallish crossbred, and chose not to submit to Leroy's restraint or my intrusion with grace. As the cow moved about, swinging its head and rear in protest, I slipped in quickly. And I felt a distinctly hard dome-shaped object bump up against my hand. I knew immediately: this one is definitely pregnant.

Although I realized that my first three verdicts were suspect, I didn't mention it. Three cows had me to thank as we released them back onto pasture; they would spend another year on the range instead of taking a trip to McDonalds. You're welcome, I murmured under my breath.

By the time we had finished checking ten head, an hour and a half had elapsed and snow was starting to blow harder. Dr M took over (not bothering with an OB glove—real cow docs are not squeamish) and had most of the herd checked before the weather warned us that we had better wash off and head back to Pullman.

This preg checking experience signaled the last of my large animal experience, and I was thankful to have survived intact. This last snowstorm also signaled the end of hard winter, and while the winds were still chilly and the fields were muddy, spring was in sight.

31

Hope and Sunshine

From his tanned and weathered face, jeans, and boots it was obvious that John was a rancher, used to herding cows on his ranch in the Okanogan country of northeast Washington. But it wasn't one of his cattle that concerned him today. He lifted Nitro, a feisty Dachshund, onto the exam table. The dog had suddenly lost feeling and function in his rear legs, and dragged himself across the table with his front legs. As Dr. Robinette examined Nitro, pinching his toes with no visible reaction, the rancher said "You've got to get him back on his legs, doc!". Dr. Robinette responded kindly, "I'm sure you miss him around the house. We'll see what we can do to help." "Hell, Nitro ain't no house dog!", the rancher replied, "He's my best stock dog, and I need him to move my cattle around. He's got a job to do, and he needs to get back to work!"

Nitro's owner explained that his ranch was hilly and covered with brush. All he had to do was to point to a group of cattle on the hillside and Nitro would tear off, barking wildly until the cattle moved where he wanted. The fact that the cows couldn't see the little dog when it was hidden by the bushes enhanced the dog's effectiveness. Nitro certainly seemed to have enough attitude to take on a thousand pound steer.

Nitro's problem was all too common. Dachshunds have short little legs because they have been bred for defective cartilage. The long bones of the legs grow from the faulty cartilage plates at the ends of the bones, which turn to bone before the legs reach full length. But the bones of the skull, pelvis, and spine do not grow from cartilage, so they are unaffected, giving the characteristic short legs and long bodies of the breed. Unfortunately the shock-absorbing discs between the vertebrae remain as cartilage throughout life, and sooner or later the defective discs deteriorate and bulge upward against the spinal cord. If the spinal cord takes a direct hit from a sudden disc rupture, the pressure and swelling must be relieved surgically within 24 hours or the dog may become permanently paralyzed. There are paraplegic Dachshunds that use wheelchair-like carts to navigate their home, but Nitro was a working dog, and disability was not an option.

Time was of the essence, so Dr. R quickly admitted Nitro and gathered the equipment needed for a hemilaminectomy surgery. Once the dog was anesthetized, an electric bone saw and sharp-edged rongeurs were used to remove the bony covering of the spinal canal and relieve pressure on the nerves. The remaining calcified disc material was scooped out of the spinal canal, a strip of fat from the shoulder area was laid on top of the exposed spinal cord, and the soft tissue was closed. Surgery went smoothly, even routinely. But once Nitro woke up from anesthesia he still could not use his rear legs.

Dr. R was cautiously optimistic. We would have to wait until the swelling and bruising of the spinal cord went down and give the nerve cells time to start functioning again. Rehabilitation could be more difficult than the surgery.

For the first week our team took care of Nitro's needs without moving him any more than necessary. Because the bladder could not empty on its own, we needed to support his body with one hand while pressing on the bladder area with the other until the bladder emptied completely. Even with practice this always ended up soaking our shoes with urine. During the second week we assumed that the swelling had receded and encouraged

Nitro to try and support his weight, first by "towel walking" him with a towel under the abdomen to support his weight, and then with "tub therapy". We filled a bathtub with warm water and encouraged him to walk from one end of the tub to the other with the water supporting most of his weight. Nitro didn't always accept our help gracefully; as we tried to nudge him from one end of the tub to the other for the two dozenth time he would turn around and snap at us. His grouchiness was understandable; he had every right to be annoyed at his inability to control his legs. We were discouraged as well. It had been three weeks since surgery and even though feeling had returned to his toes he lacked the strength or the will to walk.

The first week of May arrived with beautiful clear warm weather, and Dr. R had a new idea. "I want you to take Nitro out to the lawn in front of Wegner Hall and let him warm his bones in the sunshine. The fresh air might do him some good." For the next week, a rotation of students carried the brown bundle of attitude out to the lawn and set him down on the grass where he could absorb the sun and watch as the stream of students went by on their way to class. Right from the start Nitro refused to stay in the spot where we left him, which required us to move with him as he dragged himself over to sniff a clump of grass or bark at passing co-eds. Within days Nitro could take a dozen steps on his own if we provided support to get him started, and by the end of a week he was wobbling all the way across the lawn to chase away people who invaded his sunbathing area. "Time to send Nitro home" came the order from Dr. R. Sometimes recovery is an attitude.

32

Prickly Situations

May arrived, and the sun was finally warming the WSU campus. The caseload in both large and small animal clinics was in a lull, allowing plenty of time to look in on surgery, wander the small animal wards to read the medical records of the patients, and study for the upcoming National Board Exams.

I had one more week in the large animal barn, which left no permanent memory except for Thor. When I saw his name on the treatment board, I pictured a formidable bull or an unruly stallion. The board listed only "walk twenty minutes, three times a day", which told me that Thor was not a cow or a sheep. Walking out to stall A3, I saw my new patient: A beautiful, majestic Great Dane, wagging his tail and bouncing energetically around in the hay bedding of his stall. The barns were normally off limits to dogs, so I asked about his story.

Thor had suffered from a skin condition that could not be cured by any of a succession of referring vets. He had lost all of his hair except a little on his head, and his bare skin was thickened, smelly, flaky, and darkly discolored. His owners had reached the end of their willingness to seek answers, and when they finally brought him to the veterinary school they didn't want to try any more diagnostic tests or unproven treatments. Nothing had helped, and Thor seemed to feel depressed and unwell.

At this point the owners no longer could stand looking at their once-beautiful dog, so they "donated" him to the vet school for study (and so that their consciences could be eased for giving up on him). Veterinarians, patron saints of lost causes that they are, never want to admit that they are powerless to help a patient. Our dermatologist, petite blonde Dr Taylor, was the only woman veterinarian on staff and the youngest, having graduated from Michigan State two years early. Most of the students were older than her and she struggled to earn their respect. Perhaps Thor would offer a chance to pull off an impressive cure and gain some credibility.

Dr. T couldn't pass up a challenge like Thor, but the small animal hospital didn't have room for him, since even the runs that were spacious for a Labrador or a Collie were too cramped for a dog his size. With some persuasion, Dr T talked the large animal clinic into letting her use one of their large box stalls for Thor, and the students on large animal rotation were assigned to walk Thor three times a day.

Dr T ran every test that the Clin Path lab would allow, and performed multiple biopsies, which showed the non-specific findings of hyperkeratosis and hyperpigmentation—thick, discolored skin, but nothing that revealed what the cause was. A thyroid test seemed low, but little was known about low thyroid or even what the normal values should be. One of the referring veterinarians had already tried giving the dog a human thyroid supplement, but nothing had happened. There was reason to suspect a hormone problem, however: bilaterally symmetrical hair loss, lack of inflammation or itching, and no signs of mange mites, bacteria, or fungal elements eliminated most of the other suspects. Acting on a gut feeling that the problem had to be hormonal, Dr. T decided to put the dog back on a thyroid supplement and keep increasing the dose until either she saw results or Thor started to show the side effects of thyroid overdose (weight loss, racing heartbeat). Make him better or make him sick was the plan.

It worked. As the dose of thyroid supplement increased, Thor's hair started to grow back. By the time the dose reached five times the human dose, Thor was the picture of health, a magnificent specimen with a thick glossy coat and the energy of a puppy. Hypothyroidism is a very common problem in middle-aged dogs, and we now know that even a twenty pound dog takes the same dose of hormone as a large person. Apparently the canine intestine only absorbs a small amount of the medication, and it takes a much higher dose to raise the dog's thyroid hormone to where it should be.

Thor was cured, but now he belonged to the vet school and they had no idea what to do with him. Thor was a walking advertisement for Dr. T's expertise, so she wasn't in any hurry to find another home for her star patient. Thor continued to live in his comfy box stall, visit with all of the students and doctors as they walked through the barn, and revel in several long walks around campus each day.

This is how I came to have Thor on the end of my leash on a beautiful sunny day in May. It was a joy to stroll the sidewalks and lawns in front of McCoy Hall, the Administration Building, and the student dorms. Thor knew how to put on a show; the more onlookers there were, the more he pranced along, as though he knew he was looking good. One afternoon, while walking across the triangular lawn in front of Wegner Hall, Thor lunged forward suddenly, pulling me off of my feet and dragging me a dozen feet across the grass before stopping and turning to look at me. I had the distinct impression that he found this very amusing. I looked up to see that a group of pretty co-eds were watching the whole episode, so I unceremoniously rose and trotted back to the barn with Thor. I hope you are satisfied with yourself, I scolded, but he just bumped me with his head and gave me a wet kiss.

When I described what Thor had done on our walk to other students who had walked him previously, almost all of them related that he had pulled the same trick when they walked him; he would be on his best behavior until their attention wandered, and then he would pull them off their feet and laugh at them. It was hard to be mad at him, since he had come from being a mess to being a vet school celebrity

As the end of veterinary school neared, most of my clinical duties were in Receiving, a final introduction to veterinary medicine in the examination room. When a patient was presented to the WSU Veterinary School Clinic, it was greeted by a receptionist, and after the necessary paperwork was completed I escorted the pet and owner to an exam room, took a history, and performed the initial examination. As soon as I finished, one of the doctors would come in, repeat the examination, and dismiss me while they talked with the owner.

When the case was a referral, I had very little opportunity to watch the doctor's exam room discussion, since those cases involved serious discussions with frustrated and worried owners. But there were also the routine visits, the sorts of things that I would spend much of my career doing: vaccinations, puppy and kitten visits, deworming. Perhaps it was a little late in our education to be learning to talk to pet owners while we were trying to decipher the health needs of the animal, but "client-centered" medicine wasn't a thing yet and all of our focus had been on the patient, not the person who was attached to the animal.

On my first day in Receiving, a black and white Border Collie trotted into the waiting room, his face bristling with porcupine quills. His owner, a beefy man in farmer john overalls, trailed after him, but the dog headed straight down the hall toward the examination rooms. He entered Room 2, wagged his tail, and sat down expectantly. The intern who was on duty that afternoon laughed, "You just couldn't resist, could you?" she chuckled. Then she explained that Roscoe had been coming into the Veterinary School Hospital every 3 or 4 months for several years, always as a result of a porcupine encounter. "Whenever he gets a face-full of quills," she explained, "he runs to the farmers pickup truck, hops in the back, and waits for the boss to give him a ride from his farm over in the Moscow Mountains to the vet school." The intern hinted wryly that maybe the dog was addicted to the barbiturate anesthesia that he got every time he required quill removal, but more likely he had simply learned where he got relief when he just couldn't leave the porcupines alone.

Once his owner filled out the paperwork and gave us a quick "You know what to do", I led Roscoe back to the treatment room. After the vet on duty gave him an anesthetic, I carefully pulled out each of the hundred quills with a hemostatic forceps. I was instructed not to twist the quills, as it might break off the tip and the tiny backward-pointing barbs would pull it deeper and deeper into the tissues. A buried quill might cause a festering wound, or even penetrate some vital organ deep in the body. "Check the back of the mouth thoroughly; if he swallows a quill it will cause big problems later", the doctor reminded me as he left to look at other cases

After forty-five minutes of meticulous de-quilling, Roscoe awoke quickly and we sent him home with his master. "We'll see you next time", the intern said cheerily.

My last week in Receiving ended on Friday with the most routine of office visits. A young couple, two grad students who had just moved into an apartment together, brought their new kitten in for its first visit and vaccinations. My patient was a charming ball of fluff, with long hair, Siamese coloration, and striking blue eyes. With the unflappable confidence of a kitten, she romped around the top of the examination table and batted at my stethoscope while I leaned over to look at her. Since there were no specific complaints (as students we were better prepared to discuss severe illnesses than than the needs of the healthy patient), I was at a loss of what to talk about as I performed my examination. Suddenly, however, everything changed; as I pressed my stethoscope to her tiny chest, I could hear a heart murmur. There was no doubt about it; I had listened to audiotape examples of all of the abnormal sounds that a heart could make, and this was definitely not the distinctive lup-dup that a healthy heart makes as the ventricles contract and the heart valves open and close. The kitten's heart sounded more like "lup-fwoosh", suggesting that the mitral valve that controls the one-way flow of blood from the left atrium to the left ventricle was not closing all the way, allowing blood to flow backward into the atrium when the ventricle contracted to pump blood forward into the aorta.

My heart sank, because I knew the heartbreak that a congenital heart defect would cause as the kitten grew larger and the heart was unable to keep up with the increased workload. This ball of fluff might not see her first birthday.

The young man noticed my intent look and furrowed brow, and asked if anything was wrong. I tried to act casual as I excused myself: "I would just like one of the doctors to take a listen to your kitty; I'll be right back in a minute."

Stepping out of the exam room, I explained to the intern on duty that I had discovered a heart murmur on a patient that was presented for vaccination. What should I do? "I just saw Dr. Ott in the Cardiology ward. I'll have him take a listen."

The Great Man was still an intimidating presence and I wasn't anxious to have him stamp me an "idiot", but I knew I couldn't fake it if my patient needed help.

Within a few minutes, Dr. Ott came up the hall, and while I was still out of the owner's earshot I explained the murmur that I had heard on this new kitten. "Let's take a listen", he responded as I trailed him into the room. The first thing that Dr Ott did was to pick up the little furball, perching her on his shoulder while he stroked the kitten under its chin and asked the owners a few questions. He then placed the head of his worn stethoscope over the kitten's chest. "Sounds fine. Thanks for letting me take a listen". Before returning the kitten to its owner, the Head of Small Animal Clinics lifted the kitty to his face and gave it a gentle bump on its forehead with his own wrinkled brow, set it on the exam table, gave it another scratch on the cheek, and left the room.

I tried to remain cool as I gave the kitten its first vaccination for Distemper, as well as the new vaccine that had just been released for Rhinotracheitis (the dreaded respiratory virus that I had met during my first week in the feline disease ward) and wished the kitten's owners well with the new addition to their apartment. As an afterthought I reached over and gave the little cat a few gentle strokes under the left ear.

As soon as the kitten and its new owners were escorted to the front desk I disappeared into the hallway where Dr Ott was waiting. "What was that? I know I heard a murmur! Are you sure that the heart sounded normal?" Dr. Ott didn't actually smile, but his answer was tinged with tolerance and a slight trace of amusement: "The ribs of young kittens are so flexible that if you put even a little bit too much pressure on the chest with your stethoscope it will change the shape of the heart enough to cause turbulent blood flow, which you will hear as a murmur. Just use a lighter touch and it will go right back to the normal sound."

As Dr. Ott strolled back to the Cardiology ward, all I could do was stare after him. It wasn't that he resolved my heart concern in few seconds of listening, or that he gave me invaluable practical advice (which I would share later many times with newly graduated veterinarians that I mentored). It was that this god-like doctor, with expertise beyond what I could ever attain, who had made medical advances, published important journal articles, and ran a major veterinary school's small animal hospital, was just as content to visit with an adorable ball of fluff and reassure its apprehensive owners as he was solving a life-threatening case that had been referred to him. That lesson that would remain with me every time that I walked into an examination room.

Except for the patients that I visited in the examination room, the last month of veterinary school is a blur in my memory. I took the National Board Examination, two eight-hour days of grueling testing that covered every obscure morsel of knowledge that I was supposed to remember from the past four years, with my future livelihood hanging in the balance. There were final examinations in classes as well, but I received a gift when the professor of large animal medicine declared that we could opt to skip the final and take our current grade in the class; I had a solid C (the first C that I had since 6th grade), and I wasn't going to take a risk of worsening it by taking a test in a class in which I had barely paid attention. The senior class had a traditional Senior Skip Day for an unauthorized leave to drive down to the Snake River and drink beer, but after four years I still didn't drink and barely knew most of my classmates, so Terri and I took the day off as an opportunity to take our five-month-old son to the Spokane World's Fair on a sunny day that sang of relief after a long winter and a longer journey thru the strange territory of veterinary education.

Graduation ceremony was held on the first Saturday in June, with my family and Terri's in attendance. Two days later I walked into the examination room at Kingsgate Animal Clinic as an associate veterinarian. My first patient was an adorable eight-week old Siamese-cross kitten, for a wellness examination and its first vaccination.

33

EPILOGUE

This memoir was not a coming-of-age story. Looking back, I can see that the journey didn't change who I was; I remained socially ill at ease, anxious, and limited in my understanding of people around me. I was more comfortable with an unpredictable stallion or a surgical crisis than I was in a gathering of human beings.

But I had gained a wonderful wife, a son, and a doctor's degree in veterinary medicine. I couldn't alter who I was, but I was simply fortunate to find myself in an environment—a terrain —that used my strengths and ignored my weaknesses. How my life would have turned out in a different world is impossible to know.

Things turned out well. Three years later I built my own veterinary practice (and Terri managed it so that it was successful), where I trained a dozen young doctors, treated 50,000 dogs, cats, birds, bunnies, and a variety of injured wild animals. I was able to work with an incredible cast of veterinarians, technicians, receptionists, and kennel staff, all helping each other do the hard work that is animal medicine.

Forty-seven years later, Terri and I are still married (a rarity with vet-school marriages) and blessed with two children and five young granddaughters that we see every day. And a twenty-three-year-old long-haired black cat that we acquired from my niece with the usual "we can't keep her, Uncle Lee, but you're a veterinarian, so you can take care of her". I play music with several jazz groups and write about how lifestyle affects health and happiness in dogs and cats.

My most sincere appreciation goes to all of my teachers and classmates (I'm sorry I wasn't more fun), my patients large and small, and above all to my wife, who supported me and pretended not to notice the smell of blood and manure that followed me home. Thank you all for being in the right place with me.

ABOUT THE AUTHOR

Dr. Lee R. Harris graduated from the Washington State University College of Veterinary Medicine in 1974 and has spent more than four decades caring for pets in his own multi-doctor veterinary hospital near Seattle and at other clinics in San Diego, Phoenix, and Seattle. Dr. Harris has spoken and written extensively about cats and dogs, including articles in the Washington Post, Time Magazine, and the Houston Chronicle. Dr. Harris' previous two books, "The Good Life for Dogs: health, lifestyle, happiness and meaning" and "The Good Life for Cats: health, happiness, and living on the edge" explore how our pets' wellness is influenced by the lifestyles what we provide them.

Acknowledgements

* Peggy Kittrick provided assistance in editing and formatting.
* Bev Harris offered helpful guidance on getting the book into the hands of readers.
* Terri Culver has been my support from beginning to end.

Thank you all.